NEONATOLOGY
CLINICAL BIOCHEMISTRY

Teach thy tongue to say 'I do not know'
and thou shalt progress.

*from frontispiece to 'Retrolental Fibroplasia a
Modern Parable' by W.A. Silverman*

NEONATAL UNIT
MATERNITY UNIT
SUNDERLAND DISTRICT
HOSPITAL

CLINICAL BIOCHEMISTRY IN MEDICINE

Series Editors: Danielle B Freedman MB, BS, MRCPath
William Marshall MA, FRCP, FRCPath

NEONATOLOGY AND CLINICAL BIOCHEMISTRY

ANNE GREEN BSc, MSc, MRSC, FRCPath

Consultant Paediatric Clinical Biochemist and Head of Department of Clinical Chemistry at Birmingham Children's Hospital.

IMOGEN MORGAN MB, ChB, DCH, FRCP (G)

Consultant Neonatologist at the Regional Neonatal Unit at Birmingham Maternity Hospital.

A C B   V E N T U R E   P U B L I C A T I O N S

with generous support from Beckman Instruments (UK) Ltd,
Scientific Hospital Supplies and Wallac (UK) Ltd.

ACB VENTURE PUBLICATIONS

Managing Editor — David Burnett.

Chairman — Kevin Spencer.

CLINICAL BIOCHEMISTRY IN MEDICINE

Series Editors — Danielle B Freedman and William J Marshall.

British Library Cataloguing in Publication Data.

A catalogue record for the book is available from the British Library.

ISBN 0 902429 04 3   ACB Venture Publications

Design and Illustration — Michael Cartwright, Neil Parkes and Lorenzo Wood.

Printed by Piggotts Printers (Cambridge) Ltd.

Preface

A Clinical Biochemist and Neonatologist are perhaps not the most obvious combination of professionals to write a joint book! We are therefore grateful to the Association of Clinical Biochemists for providing the stimulus for us to get together to write on this topic and are proud to be contributing to their Clinical Biochemistry and Medicine series of ACB Venture publications.

The purpose of the book is to bring together those aspects of clinical biochemistry which are particularly relevant to the care of the neonate. The book is intended to provide essential background information and a practical approach to problems; we hope it will be of use to both junior doctors and clinical biochemists, particularly those working in non-specialist environments.

We are extremely grateful to many of our clinical colleagues and the staff in the Clinical Chemistry and Neonatology Departments at both Birmingham Children's and Birmingham Maternity Hospitals for their help with some of the details in the text and for reading numerous drafts.

We are indebted to Danielle Freedman and William Marshall, the series editors, for their forbearance and editorial skill.

Without the enormous help from our secretaries Edith Green and Becky Mitchell, this monograph would not have been accomplished and we thank them both most sincerely for their hard work. Finally, and not least, our husbands, David and David, for their unstinting support and understanding. Numerous reports on the Dining Room table and a surfeit of Marks & Spencers' meals have been the norm for many months!

July 1993
AG and MEIM.

ACKNOWLEDGEMENTS

The Authors are grateful to the following for permission to reproduce or adapt material for certain figures used in this publication:

Annals of Clinical Biochemistry 1988; **25**: 199-209 (Fig 6.4).

American Association of Clinical Chemistry, Paediatric Clinical Chemistry, 2nd Edition, Editor, Samuel Meites (Table 10.3).

British Medical Association, A-Dahrah *et al*, Arch Dis Childhood 1988; **25**: 398-402 (Fig 2.5) and Arch Dis Childhood 1992; **67**: 868-9 (Table 1.2).

Butterworth and Heinemann, Scientific Foundations of Paediatrics 1084, Editors Davis J A and Dobbing J, data derived from Widdowson E M, Changes in body proportions and composition during growth (Fig 2.3).

Churchill Livingstone, The Inherited Metabolic Diseases 1987, Editor John B Holton (Fig 6.6), Paediatric Haematology 1977, Michael L N Willoughby (Fig 10.1), Textbook of Neonatology 1986, Roberton N R C (Fig 2.4a).

Gairdner D and Pearson J, A growth chart for premature and other infants, Arch Dis Child 1971; **46**: 783-787, and Castlemead Publications chart reference GPB3 (Boys) and GPG3 (Girls) (Fig 2.1).

Drs A Coe and D R Paul of Walsgrave Hospital, Coventry for Fig 6.2.

Dr Mario Werner and John Wiley and Sons, Microtechniques for the Clinical Laboratory; Concepts and Applications 1976, (Fig 10.1 and Protocol A, Fig 2).

Dr Neil McLellan of Selly Oak Hospital, Birmingham for permission to reproduce the photograph in Fig 6.10.

Daren and Suzanne Bird (Fig 4.1).

Hodder and Stoughton Ltd, Paediatric Vade Mecum, 12th Edition, Editor Jack Insley, 1990 (Figs 3.1, 3.5 and 3.6).

J B Lippincot Co, Philadelphia, Neonatology, Editor Avery G B, 1981 (Fig 9.1).

Mark Allen Publishing Ltd, Brit J Hosp Med 1989; **41**: 426-434 (Figs 6.1 and 6.5).

Professor C H Rodeck, University College London Medical School, Rodeck C H and Nicolini U, British Medical Bulletin 1988; **44**: 826-849 (Fig 2.4b).

S Karger AG, Basel, Koch G and Wendel, Biol Neonate 1968; **12**: 136-161 (Table 9.2).

The Lancet Ltd, Blumenfield T A, Turi G K, Blanc W A, Lancet 1979; Feb 3: 230-33 (Protocol A, Fig1).

CONTENTS

Chapter 1

Introduction to Neonatal Care

NORMAL BABIES

In the United Kingdom, there are around 700000 births annually, of which 98% occur in hospital. Most of these babies will have no obstetric or neonatal problems. Around 60% will be breast fed initially and the rest will be offered a formula milk modified to resemble breast milk in chemical composition. They will go home from their maternity unit at any time between six hours and six days after birth, the timing depending on the mother's previous experience and on the delivery. After that their care will be supervised by a community midwife and their general practitioner.

They will lose up to 10% of their birth weight by the third day, predominantly due to water loss. After this, having established their feeding pattern, their weight will start to increase steadily again so that they have regained their birth weight by 10 days of age.

About one third of babies will develop mild jaundice, first apparent after 24 hours of age, but this will have gone in most babies by 10 days of age (slightly longer in a breast fed baby).

Babies whose weight lies below the 10th centile for the gestation (small for gestational age), are more at risk of hypoglycaemia in the early postnatal period than their appropriately grown fellows. This group will be offered a milk feed shortly after birth and at frequent (three hourly) intervals thereafter for the first 2-3 days. Their blood glucose will be monitored using BM-Stix (p 41). Similar monitoring is required for the infants of diabetic mothers.

Between the 6th and 10th day of life, if the baby is well and feeding normally, he will have a capillary blood specimen taken by the midwife — either in hospital or in the community — for a metabolic screening test (p 77).

Table 1.1   Useful definitions

Neonate	A live born baby less than one month old
Premature/pre-term	A baby born before 37 completed weeks gestation (timed from the start of the last menstrual period).
Extreme pre-term	A baby born before 30 weeks gestation. The majority of such babies require intensive care. There is no fixed lower gestation limit for survival, but mortality rates are very high at 24 weeks and it is very unusual for a baby to survive if born before 24 weeks.
Term	A baby born between 37 and 42 completed weeks gestation.
Postmature/post-term	A baby born after 42 weeks gestation.
Low birth weight	Birth weight <2.5kg. The proportion is variable depending on social and ethnic mix but averages about 7% in the UK.
Very low birth weight	Birth weight <1.5kg. This represents about 1% of births. Two thirds of deaths of normally formed infants fall in this group. There is no arbitrary lower weight limit for survival, but very few babies <500g survive.
Extreme low birth weight	Birth weight <1kg. 3 per 1000 births. A very high risk group.
Small for gestational age	A loose definition. A baby whose weight falls below the 10th centile for population norms at a given gestation. Some authors use 3rd centile or less than -2SD.
Large for gestational age	A baby whose weight falls above the 90th centile for population norms at a given gestation. Some authors use 97th centile or +2SD.

BABIES REQUIRING SPECIAL OR INTENSIVE CARE

WHAT IS A NEONATAL UNIT?

For 30 years now, babies with particular nursing or medical requirements in the neonatal period have been brought together into Special Care Baby Units, now more usually known as Neonatal Units. The desire to avoid unnecessary separation from mothers has meant that admission to Neonatal Units is limited to those who will require these facilities, usually less than 10% of live births. Nursing staff in such units will have specialised experience and qualifications in neonatal care; medical staffing is usually by paediatricians who spend all or part of their time in neonatal care. A number of specialised terms are used to classify groups of newborn babies (Table 1.1). The dependency and degree of illness of the babies is reflected in the clinical category of care they require. These are summarised in Table 1.2.

REASONS FOR ADMISSION

On average, each maternity unit will reserve 5 cots per 1000 deliveries for babies requiring special care and an additional 1.5 cots per 1000 for babies requiring intensive care.

About 1 in 100 babies will require intensive care from delivery, the rest of those being admitted to Neonatal Units will require only special care. In some cases, the need for intensive care can be anticipated and the mother may then be delivered in a hospital housing a neonatal intensive care unit. This is likely to be a unit with 4-6000 deliveries per annum and may mean transferring the mother during pregnancy, or just before or during labour (Table 1.3).

Babies requiring more nursing care than can be offered in the ordinary wards, babies requiring investigations and babies needing oxygen therapy or intravenous drips will all need to be admitted to a Neonatal Unit (Table 1.4).

PREMATURE BABIES

The majority of babies cared for in any Neonatal Unit will be normally formed infants who have been born prematurely.

Although there are regional variations related to social class and environment, on average 7 per 100 pregnancies will result in a baby who is low birth weight (<2.5kg) and 7 per 1000 pregnancies in a baby who is very low birth weight (<1.5kg). All babies too small to maintain body temperature in an ordinary ward

Table 1.2 Clinical categories of neonatal care

Level 1. Intensive care	Level 2. Intensive care
• Receiving assisted ventilation and in the first 24h after its withdrawal	• Requiring total parenteral nutrition
• Of less than 27 weeks' gestation for the first 48h after birth	• Having convulsions
• With birth weight <1000g for the first 48h after birth	• Being transported by a skilled neonatal nurse
• Who require major emergency surgery for the preoperative period and post operatively for 48 hours	• With arterial line or chest drain
• On the day of death	• With respiratory disease in first 48 hours of life, FiO_2 0.4–0.6
• Being transported by a team including doctors and nurses	• Less severe recurrent apnoea
• Receiving peritoneal dialysis	• Requiring exchange transfusion alone
• Requiring exchange transfusion and have other disease processes	• More than 48h postoperative, requiring complex nursing procedures
• Severe respiratory distress in first 48 hours of life — FiO_2 >0.6	• Tracheostomy (first 2 weeks)
• Recurrent apnoea needing frequent intervention	
• Significant requirement for circulatory support	

Special care

• Continuous monitoring of respiration or heart rate or transcutaneous PO_2	• Receiving additional oxygen
• Tracheostomy (after first 2 weeks)	• Receiving i.v. glucose and electrolyte solutions
• Being tube fed	• First 24h after minor surgery
• Terminal care	• Barrier nursing
• Undergoing phototherapy	• Receiving special monitoring e.g., frequent glucose or bilirubin estimation
• Constant supervision e.g., babies born to mothers who are drug abusers	• Receiving antibiotics

(<1.7kg) will require admission. Some low birth weight babies will be nursed with their mother from the beginning (well babies between 1.7 and 2.5kg birth weight, >34 weeks gestation).

Table 1.3   Situations in which transfer of the mother to a unit with neonatal intensive care should be considered

- Gestation – <30 weeks

- Estimated birth weight – <1.25kg

- Multiple pregnancy – <32 weeks

- Severe rhesus disease

- Antenatally diagnosed congenital malformation likely to require immediate surgery

Pre-term babies, whose gestation at birth may be as low as 24 weeks, will remain on the Neonatal Unit until discharge which is generally not before the equivalent of 'term' i.e., 40 weeks gestation. For individual babies, particularly those with chronic respiratory or digestive problems, the stay can be much longer and occasionally a baby will need to remain on a Neonatal Unit for most of its first year of life.

Care may start by being very intensive, involving ventilation and parenteral nutrition then lessen as the baby improves to requiring only 'special care'. Often the mother may be readmitted just prior to the baby's discharge to prepare her for taking the baby home. The absolute numbers of very small babies cared for is increasing in all units because of improved survival and increased readiness to offer intensive care to babies of short gestation.

OUTCOME

Outcomes for small and premature babies have greatly improved over the last ten years with continuing development in obstetrics and neonatal intensive care. In our unit, a Regional referral centre, 60% of the workload involves babies between 1-2kg birth weight. Survival figures for all inborn admissions to the unit were recently as shown (Fig 1.1). The main reasons for death in the neonatal period are the presence of lethal congenital abnormality, the development of cerebral ischaemia or haemorrhage and the complications of respiratory distress syndrome (see Ch 2).

Neurological or developmental handicap of significant degree affects 8% of surviving infants of 1-1.5kg birth weight and about 17% of survivors of <1.0kg birth weight. This may be deafness, visual impairment, cerebral palsy or severe developmental delay.

The incidence of cerebral palsy in surviving babies has not fallen as expected in recent years and currently it is thought that much of it is determined antenatally.

'Cot deaths' are increased in premature infants. The reasons for this are probably multifactorial.

Table 1.4   Criteria for admission to the Neonatal Unit

Babies requiring admission

• Severe birth asphyxia	• Obvious congenital abnormality which will require early surgery
• <1.7kg birth weight	• <34 weeks gestation
• Babies who appear ill requiring investigation and treatment	• Cyanosis
• Hypoglycaemia in a baby which has not recovered after a feed or who cannot be fed	• At risk because of maternal illness
• Dying babies	• Postoperative babies (may be specialised surgical unit)
• Babies requiring total parental nutrition (TPN)	

Babies not requiring admission

• Babies who have been delivered operatively who are well	• Babies who have had low Apgar scores but who have clinically recovered
• Well babies of >1.7kg and <2.5kg birth weight and >34 weeks gestation	• Babies with cleft lips or palates who can feed
• Babies with Down's syndrome	• Infants of diabetic mothers who are well
• Small for gestational age babies (unless <1.7kg birth weight)	

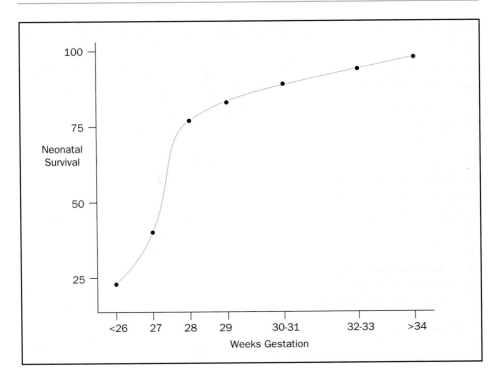

Fig 1.1   **Survival of admissions during 1989 to the Neonatal Unit, Birmingham Maternity Hospital**

FURTHER READING

Fleming PJ, editor. Neonatal Vade-Mecum. 2nd rev ed. Lloyd Luke (Medical Books) Ltd, Sevenoaks, 1986.

Gandy GM, Roberton NRC. Lecture notes on Neonatalogy. Blackwell Scientific Publications, Oxford, 1987.

Harlow N, Roberts R, Cooke R W. Outcome at 5 years for children with birth weights of 1250g or less. Arch Dis Ch. 1992; **68**: 286-290.

Roberton NRC, editor. Textbook of Neonatology. 2nd edition. Churchill Livingstone, Edinburgh, 1992.

Chapter 2

Physiology of the Newborn

GROWTH

Babies of low birth weight have long been known to be at increased risk of illness and death. Since the 1960s, babies who are of short gestation have been distinguished from those who are growth restricted. Charts are now available (Fig 2.1) showing the range of weights for infants at each week of gestation. A baby of a given weight may be appropriately grown at (for instance) 34 weeks gestation, but would be described as small for dates (SFD), or small for gestational age (SGA) if born at term.

In the United Kingdom, about one third of all babies born weighing <2.5kg are SGA. In countries where nutrition and living standards are much poorer, the proportion of low birth weight babies may be up to 50%, of which two thirds may be SGA. SGA babies may be congenitally small individuals (10% of the normal population) or they may have become growth retarded *in utero*.

Fetal growth retardation may be diagnosed during pregnancy by clinical examination and ultrasound monitoring. Fetal health can be monitored in 'at risk' patients ultrasonically, by measuring growth, assessing blood flow patterns to and within the fetus, and estimating fetal wellbeing by looking at fetal breathing and movements and the amount of liquor surrounding the fetus. If intervention is needed for the high risk fetus, delivery (usually by caesarean section) can then be optimally timed.

After birth, in well babies, birth weight will be regained by the 10th day and thereafter growth proceeds at an average of 6g/kg/day for the first month. In babies who are ill or whose nutritional intake is limited, growth postnatally may cease for several weeks then resume at a reduced rate. Babies who have been born at 28 weeks gestation or less, commonly weigh only 2 to 2.5kgs on reaching the equivalent of full term. This early postnatal growth appears to be genetically and nutritionally determined.

Babies who have become growth retarded late in pregnancy, commonly from placental dysfunction, can demonstrate dramatic 'catch up' growth in the first three months postpartum, and if fed *ad libitum* will consume 220-250mL/kg/day compared to the usual 150mL/kg/day of milk.

Conversely, very large babies, usually those whose mothers are grand multiparae or who have diabetes or glucose intolerance, grow poorly postnatally and have a relatively small appetite ('catch down').

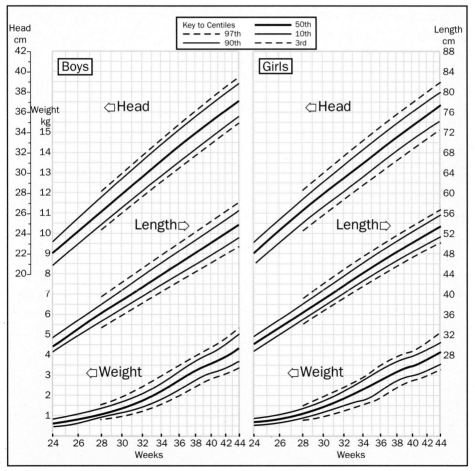

Fig 2.1   **Standard charts for head size, length and weight for boys and girls**

CIRCULATORY ADAPTION AT BIRTH

Before birth, the 'fetoplacental unit' has a blood volume of 105mL/kg, about 30% of which is in the placenta. The fetal heart pumps deoxygenated blood from the systemic circulation, via the two umbilical arteries to the placenta. After oxygenation, the blood returns via the umbilical vein to the inferior vena cava and the right atrium of the heart (Fig 2.2). Very little blood is required to go through the high pressure pulmonary circulation. Most blood passes through the foramen ovale (a valve-like flap) from the right side of the heart (which is at slightly higher pressure than the left), to the left side of the circulation. The rest goes from the right ventricle via the pulmonary artery through the patent ductus arteriosus to the ascending aorta and the systemic circulation. A little blood (about 7% in total) goes through the pulmonary circulation returning to the left side of the heart. The design of this circulation allows the blood with the highest oxygen content to reach the left ventricle and thence the coronary arteries and the brain.

After birth, two major factors promote circulatory changes. These are the clamping or constriction of the umbilical cord and the baby's first breath.

Cutting off the placental bed leads to a rise in the systemic and pulmonary pressures and provides one of several stimuli to the baby to breathe. Cerebrally stimulated gasping occurs due to early asphyxia probably acting via brainstem chemoreceptors. External factors such as temperature change and handling also stimulate gasping.

The baby uses considerable effort and generates a large negative intrathoracic pressure averaging -50cm water when he takes his first breath and the lungs fill with air. The expansion of the lungs lead to a five fold increase in pulmonary blood flow and a dramatic fall in pulmonary blood pressure. This results in the pressure in the right side of the heart falling below the pressure on the left. Flow through the foramen ovale stops and flow through the ductus reverses to become left to right. Increased pulmonary arterial oxygen tension maintains the vasodilatation in the lungs and the pulmonary pressure remains low. The ductus arteriosus shunting rapidly becomes biphasic and stops, with effective closure at 10 to 12 hours of age. In the sick or pre-term infant, however, this ductal closure can be delayed for days or weeks.

In the fetus, ductal constriction is inhibited by hypoxia and by local actions of prostaglandins E_1 and E_2. These effects can be utilized therapeutically. If an

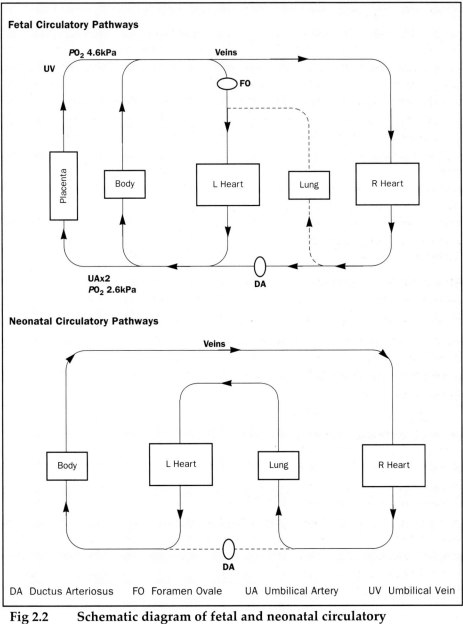

Fig 2.2 Schematic diagram of fetal and neonatal circulatory pathways. In the fetus the ventricles work in parallel.

infant has a congenital heart defect in which circulation to the aorta is dependent on a patent ductus, patency can be maintained until surgery by an infusion of prostaglandin E_2. Conversely, if a persistently patent ductus is causing circulatory problems in a pre-term infant, intravenous indomethacin, (a prostaglandin synthetase inhibitor) has an 80% probability of closing it.

THE RESPIRATORY SYSTEM

THE FETAL LUNG

Ultrasound can be used to detect the increasingly regular breathing movements made by the fetus during periods of wakefulness and activity. These movements are thought to be important for lung development. The fetal airways are filled with clear fluid containing phospholipid, which is being produced continually. When the fetus is apnoeic, there is an outflow of this fluid into the amniotic fluid around the fetus. Amniotic fluid can therefore be studied to predict lung maturity, particularly by estimation of the ratio of lecithin (phosphatidyl choline), whose production increases markedly towards the end of gestation, to sphingomyelin, whose production is more constant (L:S ratio). A ratio of 2 or above would indicate lung maturity. A ratio below 1.5 predicts surfactant deficiency (a cause of respiratory distress syndrome, see below) with 80% certainty.

Fetal breathing becomes more regular as gestation advances. Many alterations in the fetal environment can affect it, including hypoxia, maternal smoking, maternal drugs, or fetal infection.

Fetal asphyxia abolishes regular breathing and induces gasping. Breathing patterns can be assessed as part of a 'biophysical profile' of fetal wellbeing.

THE LUNG AT BIRTH

From 24 weeks gestation onwards, two distinct cell types can be found in the epithelium of the terminal air sacs. Type 1 pneumocytes are flattened and form the gas exchange surface. Type 2 pneumocytes, which are smaller, contain lamellar bodies associated with the production and excretion of surfactant. This has a number of components, the main one being dipalmitoyl phosphatidyl choline. Important connective tissue elements, which may aid lung elasticity, may depend on glucocorticoids for their maturation. The lung is filled with liquid to a volume similar to that of the resting air-filled lung in the neonate (30-35mL/kg).

At birth, lung liquid production stops. The likely cause is the adrenaline surge associated with labour. Some liquid is squeezed out of the mouth during the second stage of labour, while most is absorbed into pulmonary lymphatics and capillaries. The baby can generate extremely high, negative intrathoracic pressure to take the first breath; up to -100cm water has been recorded. After the first few breaths, resting lung volume increases rapidly. The effect of the newly released surfactant in lowering surface tension at air-fluid interfaces within the lung means that lung expansion becomes progressively easier. Airways resistance falls rapidly in the first two hours, then gradual resorption of lung liquid produces a steady increase in compliance over the first 24 hour period.

Delayed clearance of this lung liquid can lead to mild, transient respiratory distress (transient tachypnoea of the newborn). The normal baby at term breathes at a rate of 25-40 breaths per minute, with a vital capacity 35-40mL/kg. Before term, breathing effort may be periodic rather than regular. Apnoea is a common accompaniment of periodic breathing and may result from a number of factors including upper airway obstruction or a hypoventilatory response to hypoxia.

SURFACTANT
The release of surfactant from the lamellar bodies of the type 2 pneumocytes occurs in response to lung expansion. These molecules, which have a hydrophilic tail and a hydrophobic head, form a monolayer over the air-fluid interface which renews itself constantly. This has the effect of dramatically increasing pulmonary compliance and functional residual capacity. The syndrome of surfactant deficiency (idiopathic respiratory distress syndrome) is seen in the immature and also in response to insults such as hypothermia or asphyxia. It is commoner in males and in the infants of diabetic mothers. Its incidence can be reduced by the administration of glucocorticoid to the mother between 48 hours and seven days before delivery, if pre-term delivery is anticipated. This technique, however, is less effective before 27 weeks' gestation. Administration of thyrotrophin releasing hormone even a few hours before delivery may have an additive beneficial effect.

Respiratory distress syndome (RDS) is the main reason for ventilation or oxygen therapy being required in pre-term infants, and is directly or indirectly the major cause of death in this group.

It has been estimated that RDS affects 12000 babies per year in the UK, accounting for approximately 20% of the neonatal mortality. Modern neonatal intensive care has had a huge effect in reducing the mortality and morbidity of this condition and exogenous surfactant is now becoming generally available. This can be administered at delivery or within the first 24 hours into the airway of vulnerable babies and in large trials has reduced the mortality of the condition by about 40%. Exogenous surfactant can be entirely synthetic, containing dipalmitoyl phosphatidyl choline and phosphatidyl glycerol with or without a spreading agent, or it can be derived from bovine or porcine lung. The animal preparations, in general, tend to have a more rapid and pronounced effect.

Babies with RDS develop grunting, indrawing, tachypnoea and cyanosis after birth, which becomes worse over the next 24 hours. The severity varies from a need for small amounts of supplemental oxygen to the provision of full ventilatory support. In babies who survive, slow recovery begins after about 2 days. The baby begins to produce increasing amounts of endogenous surfactant and lung compliance improves. This stage is accompanied by a diuresis.

Lung recovery may be complete, but in immature or very small (<1kg) babies the lungs not uncommonly develop a fibrous reaction to oxygen and barotrauma (the effect of positive pressure ventilation) and a state of chronic oxygen dependency develops (bronchopulmonary dysplasia).

GASTROINTESTINAL FUNCTION AND NUTRITION

THE GASTROINTESTINAL TRACT

Structural development of the fetal gastrointestinal tract is virtually complete by 20 weeks. Functional development is very limited before 26 weeks, which is one reason why nutrition by the enteral route is difficult in the most immature babies (see p 128). Enteral nutrition with human milk will not supply some nutrients at the rate at which normal intrauterine accretion is calculated. Thus if the pre-term infant is fed mature human milk or standard formula milk, intakes of calcium, phosphate and iron will be well below intrauterine rates.

Vitamin concentrations in the blood of the neonate are equivalent to or above those of the mother with the exception of vitamin E. Stores of all vitamins, however, are low in the premature infant since most of the transport to the fetus occurs in the third trimester.

Intermediary metabolism is also suboptimal in the pre-term infant, with development late in fetal life of the enzymes converting methionine to cysteine, cysteine to taurine and phenylalanine to tyrosine as well as those concerned with the further catabolism of tyrosine. The pre-term infant is therefore at risk of accumulation of methionine, tyrosine and phenylalanine, while having increased requirements for cysteine and taurine. These considerations, along with others, e.g., the need for a high calorie intake in limited volume, the need for extra minerals and vitamins and the need for extra protein in a digestible form, have led to the development of specific infant formulae for low birth weight or pre-term babies who are not receiving breast milk, or the fortification of breast milk for those who are.

ADAPTATION TO ENTERAL NUTRITION
Babies born after 34 weeks gestation can usually co-ordinate sucking and swallowing sufficiently for full oral nutrition. Before this, complete or partial feeding by nasogastric tube is usually necessary.

The first enteral feeds trigger key postnatal changes in gut structure and function; surges occur in a number of gut hormones. Their precise effects are unknown but enteroglucagon and gastrin have trophic effects to gut mucosa and motilin has an effect in increasing gut motor activity. The pancreatic glucagon surge may switch on hepatic enzyme synthesis, including phosphoenolpyruvate carboxykinase (required for gluconeogenesis) and tyrosine aminotransferase (required for tyrosine catabolism). Lactose containing feeds may increase gut lactase content; high protein diets may increase pancreatic trypsinogen and lipase in the pre-term infant; while intestinal secretions and the development of an intestinal flora may also influence gut development.

Conversely, parenteral nutrition with no enteral feeds has been demonstrated to produce intestinal mucosal atrophy with reduction in the activity of brush border enzymes.

LIVER FUNCTION
The metabolism and excretion of many exogenous and endogenous substances by the liver proceeds at a slower rate in the newborn than in the older child or adult and part of the systems immaturity of the pre-term baby is immaturity of hepatic function. The most obvious effect of this is the appearance of jaundice in up to one third of all newborn babies, so called 'physiological jaundice' (See p 23).

Table 2.1   Effects of neonatal liver dysfunction

• Accumulation of drugs	• Accumulation of metabolites
• Deficient synthesis of proteins e.g., albumin	• Jaundice
• Association with vitamin K depletion to produce haemorrhagic disease of the newborn	• Toxic effect of unconjugated bilirubin on the neonatal brain (kernicterus)
• Biliary 'sludging' in the liver in presence of excess bilirubin load e.g., due to haemolytic processes	

Liver dysfunction can be important in the newborn because it reflects underlying disease, e.g., neonatal hepatitis, or structural abnormality e.g., biliary atresia. It also produces a number of other effects in addition to jaundice (Table 2.1)

BODY FLUIDS

NEONATAL BLOOD

At birth, the baby's plasma in many respects resembles maternal plasma in composition, with modifications due to placental action. Many biochemical parameters will reflect those of the mother at that time and any abnormality — for instance increased creatinine — may take several days to return to normal due to the low neonatal glomerular filtration rate. Calcium and phosphate concentrations will be slightly higher than maternal values because of placental effects. Alkaline phosphatase activity (total) may be elevated to >1000IU because of the presence of placental isoenzyme.

Concentrations of plasma proteins which are not freely diffusible across the placenta are very variable and reflect intrauterine nutrition, maturity and fetal wellbeing. Albumin concentration, for instance, may be as low as 20g/L in a growth retarded pre-term baby, or as high as 40g/L in a healthy full term infant.

In the immediate post delivery period, there is a shift of fluid from the vascular to the extravascular compartment and a decrease in total plasma volume. Between 4 and 24 hours after birth, the blood volume gradually increases again. After this, plasma volume remains fairly constant at 40-50mL/kg to the end of the first week.

The volume of extracellular fluid, a total of 40% of body weight at birth in the full term infant falls to about 35% of body weight over the first five days of life, contributing to postnatal weight loss.

NEONATAL BODY COMPOSITION

Knowledge of body mineral and water content is based mainly on analyses of fetuses and on isotope dilution studies in babies. Pre-term babies have extremely high total body water content as a proportion of total body weight or volume mainly as a result of increased extracellular fluid. Even at full term, a baby has a proportionally much higher water content than an older infant or adult (Fig 2.3).

Sodium and chloride content of fat free tissue is also increased and is thought to decrease gradually from fetal life to adulthood.

The fat content of the neonate is very variable, fat being largely added during the third trimester and depending on the adequacy of placental perfusion as well as maternal factors. On average a baby delivered at 28 weeks will contain 3.5% fat, a baby of 34 weeks 7-8% and a full term baby 15%.

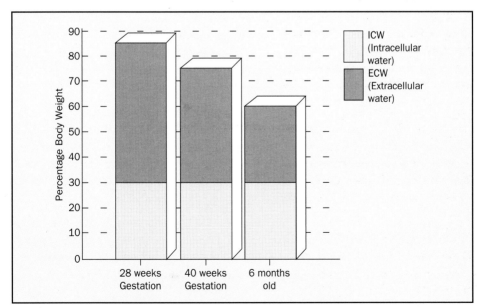

Fig 2.3　　**Body water as a percentage of body weight in the fetus, the neonate and the infant**

The total blood volume of the baby averages 80mL/kg but can be affected at delivery by whether the cord is clamped immediately or after a delay, as up to one third of the blood volume of the feto-placental unit is within the placenta and up to half of this may be transferred to the baby in the minute after birth if the infant is held below the level of the placenta. The cord haemoglobin concentration averages 16.8g/dL at term with a range of 14 to 20g/dL. The haemoglobin rises in the first hours after birth as the plasma volume falls, then returns to the cord blood value by the age of one week. In term babies about 70-80% of total haemoglobin is haemoglobin F (HbF), but the proportion is higher in babies born prematurely. By six months of age, the percentage of HbF has decreased to 1%.

RENAL SYSTEM

THE FETAL KIDNEYS

Rapid developmental changes occur in almost all the organs involved in salt and water transport up to about 35 weeks gestation; the result is that disturbances of metabolism are commoner in infancy than later in life, and in pre-term than in term infants. Urine is produced by the developing fetus from about the ninth week of gestation. Since toxin elimination is by the placenta, the function of urine production is uncertain, however, the major one is likely to be the maintenance of a cushion of fluid around the fetus, allowing swallowing, breathing and limb and trunk movements to occur. The urine is high in volume and in sodium content, resembling a plasma ultrafiltrate. (Fig 2.4a and b).

Information about fetal urine is now becoming increasingly available as the fetal bladder can be punctured under ultrasound control and urine sampled without interfering with the pregnancy. Biochemical parameters of such urine, particularly sodium and creatinine concentration, may be of some use in assessing fetal renal function. This can be very useful if the renal tract is obstructed *in utero* and early surgery might help the baby.

Nephrogenesis is complete by the 35th or 36th week, though the nephrons continue to mature for a long period after this. As far as control of salt and water excretion is concerned, infants born before 35 weeks gestation behave differently from those born at term, in particular having poorer tubular function.

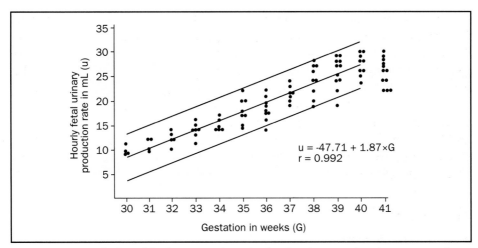

Fig 2.4a   Relationship between hourly fetal urine production rate and gestational age in normal pregnancy

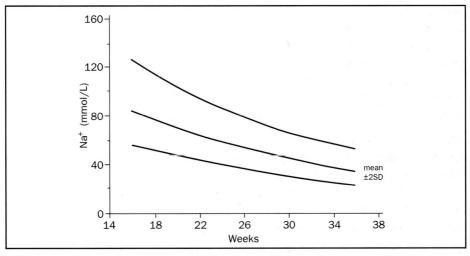

Fig 2.4b   Changes in concentration of sodium in fetal urine during gestation

RENAL FUNCTION IN THE NEONATE

Birth results in an abrupt change in renal function at all gestational ages. Urinary output shuts down sharply from fetal levels of up to 25mL hourly to values of 1to 2 mL/kg/h.

The glomerular filtration rate (GFR) is low, being only about 25% of that in older children in relation to surface area. In full term infants it increases rapidly during the first week of life, by 50-100% and thereafter more slowly, to reach adult levels (per unit surface area) by the age of two years.

The GFR in pre-term babies rises more slowly and gradually over the first month and is always significantly lower (per unit surface area) than that of full term infants.

Sodium excretion falls after birth, as the neonate is in a state of considerable sodium deficit as compared with the fetus. Full term infants who are healthy can retain sodium efficiently. Pre-term infants or asphyxiated full term infants do not appear to be able to generate effective tubular reabsorption of sodium despite being in negative balance. This will lead to continued urinary sodium losses and hyponatraemia if the baby has a low salt intake.

Tubular sodium handling can be assessed by estimating fractional sodium excretion (FE_{Na}) assuming a steady state and that creatinine (Cr) clearance equates to GFR.

$$FE_{Na}\% = \frac{[Na]_u}{[Na]_p} \times \frac{[Cr]_p}{[Cr]_u} \times 100$$

Where u and p refer to urine and plasma concentrations respectively.

This value has been estimated as about 13% in the fetal kidney between 13-18 weeks gestation, 5% in the 32-36 week fetus and 3.5% in the term fetus (Fig 2.5). After birth, sodium and water conservation is necessary and at all gestational ages FE_{Na} decreases rapidly after birth. In babies born at term, it is 0.3% or less by day three. In pre-term babies it may be 2-5% for the first week despite negative sodium balance and a low salt intake. During this period extracellular fluid and total body water fall quite considerably. The mechanism of change to conservation of salt and water at birth is thought to involve several mediators including catecholamines, vasopressin, renin, angiotensin, aldosterone and prostaglandins. In pre-term infants, plasma renin, angiotensin II and aldosterone concentrations are all high and continuing salt loss suggests renal tubular unresponsiveness to these mediators.

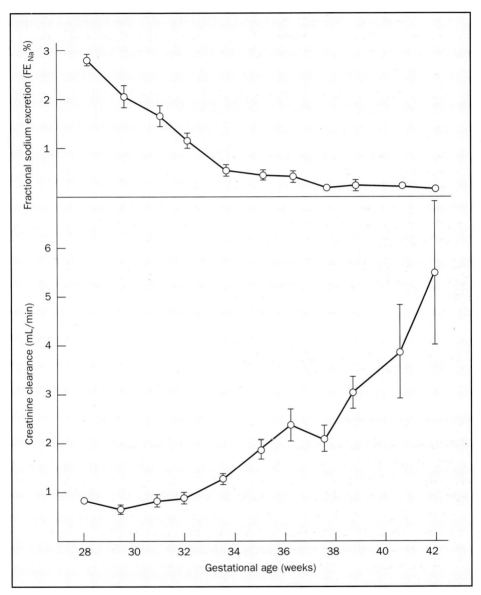

Fig 2.5   **Fractional sodium excretion and glomerular filtration rate (Mean ± 1 SEM) as a function of gestational age**

Urinary diluting capacity is good at birth but the ability to excrete a water load is limited by the low GFR. The capacity to concentrate urine is low, increasing only slowly during the first two years of life. Timed or complete urine collections are difficult to obtain in the newborn. This has led to the frequent use of urinary creatinine concentration as a yardstick against which to measure normal excretion rates of other compounds. Normal urinary excretion rates of creatinine have been determined from a large group of pre-term and term newborn infants. Excretion of endogenous creatinine correlated with weight has a median value of 90 μmol/kg/24h and a range (±2 SD) of 45-180 μmol kg/24h at all gestations.

INSENSIBLE WATER LOSSES

Transepidermal water loss can be very large in the most immature babies, due to the thinness of the skin and the lack of a keratinised layer and will be exacerbated if overhead radiant heaters are used to maintain body temperature. Losses are 15 fold higher at 25-28 weeks gestation than at term. Although they decrease rapidly in the first few postnatal days, they remain higher than in the term infant. Losses on day one as high as 200mL/kg have been recorded. Lack of attention to this in management can result in circulatory and renal failure, as well as significant hypernatraemia and haemoconcentration.

Respiratory losses of water are significant if there is tachypnoea with respiratory distress or if the environment is poorly humidified. Usually about two thirds of insensible loss is transepidermal and one third from the respiratory tract.

FURTHER READING

Milner A D, Vyas H. Lung expansion at birth. J Peds 1982; **101**: 879-886.

Milner A D. How does exogenous surfactant work? Arch Dis Ch. 1993; **68**: 253-254.

Murphy J D, Rabinowitz H, Goldstein J D, Reid L M. Structural basis of persistent pulmonary hypotension in the newborn infant. J Peds 1981; **98**: 962-967.

Nelson K B. What proportion of cerebral palsy is related to birth asphyxia? J Peds 1988; **112**: 572-574.

Rodeck CH, Nicolini U. Physiology of the mid-trimester fetus. BrMed Bull 1988; **44**: 826-849.

Chapter 3

The Term Infant: Clinical and Biochemical Problems

INTRODUCTION

The majority of term infants require no clinical chemistry input. The commonest problems requiring investigation are jaundice and suspected hypoglycaemia. Monitoring of infants on intravenous fluids who may have damage to organ systems, e.g., renal failure, or those on drugs affecting electrolyte balance, and the investigation of the acutely ill infant who may have a metabolic disorder, will be required much less frequently.

Facilities for blood gas analysis are an essential component in the provision of neonatal care, being required for the measurement of cord blood pH, the monitoring of the sick infant on oxygen therapy, and for the investigation of unexpected acidosis.

JAUNDICE (see also Chapter 4)

OCCURRING IN THE FIRST TEN DAYS OF LIFE.

CAUSES AND TREATMENT.
Up to 50% of normal babies develop 'physiological' jaundice after 48h of age. Total bilirubin does not usually increase above 200µmol/L and usually falls to normal by the 7th–10th day. Almost all the bilirubin is unconjugated bilirubin with 'direct reacting' bilirubin being no more than 40µmol/L. These babies are well and thriving and require no treatment.

An exaggerated rise in bilirubin may be seen if the baby is bruised or has, for example, a cephalohaematoma, each gram of haemoglobin yielding 600 micromoles of bilirubin on breakdown. Other causes include dehydration due to inadequate fluid intake, infection, polycythaemia at delivery, breastfeeding or use of oxytocins during delivery (Table 3.1).

Table 3.1 Pathological factors aggravating physiological jaundice

• Prematurity	• Infections	• Inadequate calories
• Dehydration	• Hypoxia	• Meconium retention
• Haemolysis	• Hypoglycaemia	• Intestinal obstruction
• Polycythaemia	• Hypothyroidism	

Severe unconjugated hyperbilirubinaemia incurs a risk of kernicterus. To prevent this, treatment such as phototherapy or exchange transfusion is required, treatment being instituted according to the guidelines in Fig. 3.1.

Jaundice which appears unusually early (i.e., within first 24h), or is severe enough to require phototherapy, requires investigation for the presence of haemolysis. Determination of maternal and infant blood groups, direct Coombs' testing of infant blood, full blood count and, if the baby is Mediterranean, African or Asian in origin, measurement of glucose 6-phosphate dehydrogenase are all indicated. Urine should be screened for infection, reducing sugars and the presence of bilirubin.

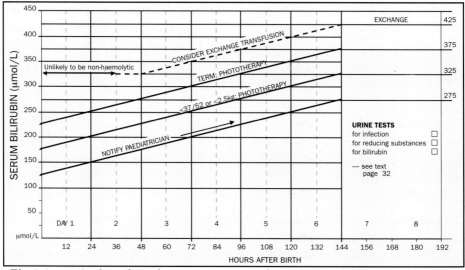

Fig 3.1   Action chart for management of non-haemolytic jaundice in the neonate

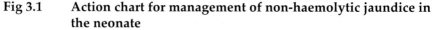

The goal of treatment is to reduce the level of unconjugated bilirubin in the blood, with the aim of thereby reducing the risk of cerebral damage (kernicterus) due to bilirubin. Features of kernicterus include fits, lethargy and opisthotonic posturing which may be seen if the plasma bilirubin concentration exceeds 500μmol/L. Adequate hydration, which may involve tube feeding or an intravenous infusion, together with phototherapy, will usually avert the need for exchange transfusion for non-haemolytic jaundice. Bilirubin may need to be monitored 4-6 hourly initially and an appropriate service for bilirubin measurement is required (see Ch. 10, p 160). If the bilirubin rises above a predetermined concentration (see Fig. 3.1) an exchange transfusion must be performed. An umbilical arterial or venous catheter can by used to give and remove blood in 20mL aliquots, or blood can be removed from a peripheral arterial cannula while donor blood runs into a contralateral vein. A total of twice the baby's blood volume (i.e.,160 mL/kg) of whole blood is exchanged over a minimum of two hours. After the procedure, 10% calcium gluconate (1mL/kg) is routinely given to the baby to counteract the effect of the CPD (citrate phosphate dextrose) in the blood.

HAEMOLYTIC DISORDERS

A number of conditions can cause excessive breakdown of red cells in the fetus and neonate. These may present as early neonatal jaundice or, if more severe, as anaemia from birth if the rate of haemolysis is greater than the rate of red cell production.

Intrinsic red cell abnormalitites producing anaemia which can present at this time include spherocytosis, an autosomal dominant condition with excessive red cell fragility, and red cell enzyme abnormalities, the common ones being glucose 6-phosphate dehydrogenase deficiency and pyruvate kinase deficiency. Haemoglobinopathies do not usually present as neonatal jaundice. Acquired defects producing haemolysis include both intrauterine and postnatal infections. The commonest causes, however, of haemolytic disease of the newborn are blood group incompatibilities between mother and fetus.

Glucose 6-phosphate dehydrogenase deficiency

Glucose 6-phosphate dehydrogenase (G6PD) deficiency is an X-linked disorder which is associated with drug induced haemolytic crises and neonatal jaundice. The disease is expressed in males and homozygous females. Female heterozygotes are not usually affected clinically, although they can have mild problems. The disorder occurs most frequently in persons of Mediterranean, African and Asian origin, with an incidence as high as 20% in some populations. The incidence in Northern Europe and Japan is very low.

A significant number (20-30%) of G6PD deficient infants develop neonatal jaundice. The jaundice occurs spontaneously without drug contact and can occur in the full term as well as the pre-term infant. It usually occurs by the 2nd-3rd day of life and usually subsides by the end of the first week. The timing of the jaundice may be later or extended if there is additional drug contact. Affected neonates may also become jaundiced after contact with one of the offending drugs through the placenta, in breast milk or after contact with clothes impregnated with naphthalene (mothballs). A large number of drugs including antimalarials, antibiotics and analgesics can precipate haemolysis. The possibility of G6PD deficiency should be considered in jaundiced newborns of either sex with immigrant parents.

Blood Group Incompatibility
The most important causes of neonatal jaundice are fetal-maternal blood group incompatibility involving the ABO system, the Kell system and the Rhesus system. This last group can present with very severe disease (hydrops fetalis) or even produce fetal death. All Rhesus negative pregnant women are screened for the presence of antibody at booking and again at 28 weeks gestation. If they have no antibodies, they will be given Rhesus immunoglobulin after delivery to prevent antibody development. If antibodies develop during pregnancy, or the level rises, this indicates that the fetus is likely to be Rhesus positive and at risk of being affected. Screening of fetal wellbeing will include serial amniocenteses to detect the presence of bilirubin metabolites by measurement of the optical density of the liquor at 450nm (Fig. 3.2). This can be performed from 22 weeks gestation onwards. If the baby is likely to be significantly affected, intervention to treat fetal anaemia can be performed. This will nowadays involve sampling fetal blood from the umbilical vein with ultrasound guidance, then transfusion of adult Rhesus negative blood into this vessel if the fetal haemoglobin is low. Severely affected babies may be electively delivered prematurely to allow immediate postnatal exchange transfusion.

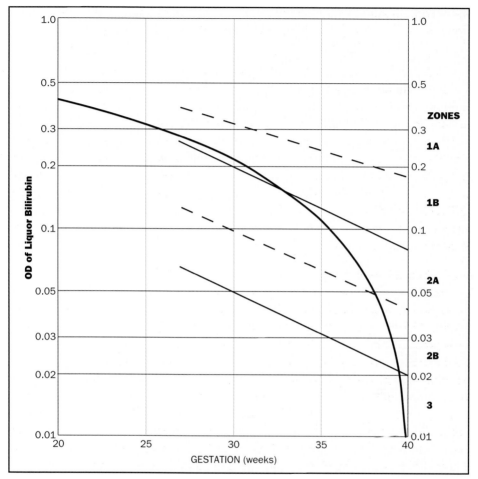

Fig 3.2 Correlation of OD liquor bilirubin with gestation. The straight lines indicate Liley's zones of disease severity. The curved line is Whitfield's action line for transfusion or delivery

PROLONGED JAUNDICE

CONJUGATED VS UNCONJUGATED BILIRUBIN

Jaundice presenting or persisting after 10 days in the term baby is abnormal. It is important to perform some measurement to assess bilirubin conjugation, e.g., direct reacting bilirubin and to consider the diagnoses listed on Table 3.2.

Table 3.2   Causes of prolonged or late presenting jaundice

Disorder	Type of Jaundice	Supporting information	Further investigations
Breast feeding	U	Jaundice spontaneously resolves if breast feeding withdrawn. No clinical or biochemical evidence of liver dysfunction	
Infection	C/U	Improves with treatment	Infection screen (see Table 3.3) Urine culture
Rhesus/ABO isoimmunisation	C	History of early haemolytic jaundice	
Total parenteral nutrition (TPN)	C	History of TPN	Nil if resolves after TPN has been discontinued
Biliary atresia	C	Pale stools	Liver ultrasound/DISIDA scan
Alpha$_1$-anti antitrypsin deficiency	C		Plasma alpha$_1$-antitrypsin phenotyping
Hypothyroidism	U	Clinical signs	TSH, free T4 (see p. 83)
Intrahepatic biliary disease:— Alagille syndrome	C	Characteristic facies Congenital abnormalities:— Pulmonary artery hypoplasia	Hypoplasia or reduced intrahepatic bile ducts on liver biopsy
Galactosaemia	C	Cataracts Urinary reducing substances +ve	Erythrocyte galactose 1-phosphate uridyl transferase (see p. 113)
Tyrosinaemia type I	C	Hypoglycaemia, abnormal clotting Alkaline phosphatase increased	Plasma amino acids (tyrosine & methionine) Urine succinylacetone (see p. 104)
Zellweger's syndrome	C	Hypotonia Dysmorphic features Neurological dysfunction	Plasma very long chain fatty acids
Glucose 6-phospate dehydrogenase deficiency	U	Usually presents early Drug induced family history Mediterranean, Asian or African race	Erythrocyte glucose 6-phosphate dehydrogenase
Crigler-Najjar types I & II	U	No liver dysfunction Type II responds to phenobarbitone	Glucuronides in bile Glucuronyl transferase in liver
Cystic fibrosis	C	Meconium ileus	Plasma/blood spot immunoreactive trypsin Sweat Na and Cl

C= Conjugated U= Unconjugated
DISIDA= Diisopropyliminodiacetic acid

There are four bilirubin fractions in plasma:

- unconjugated bilirubin (alpha)

- monoglucuronide conjugate (beta)

- diglucuronide conjugate (gamma)

- an albumin bound fraction (delta)

Most laboratories measure 'direct reacting' bilirubin as a measure of conjugation. Commonly available methods are non-specific and a direct reacting fraction of up to 40μmol/L can be found in normal babies who are jaundiced. However, in the baby with prolonged jaundice a concentration of 'direct reacting' bilirubin greater than 15% of the total bilirubin is abnormal.

Some dry chemistry methods (e.g., those employed in Kodak instruments) allow more specific measurement of the unconjugated and conjugated bilirubin fractions. In normal neonates with physiological jaundice there is very little (<10 μmol/L) conjugated bilirubin. The presence of urinary bilirubin (detected, e.g., by Ictotest or Ictostix (Ames)) is indicative of conjugated hyperbilirubinaemia.

BREAST FEEDING AND JAUNDICE

Plasma bilirubin concentration tends to be higher in breast fed than in bottle fed infants, but usually the difference is minimal. However in an estimated 2.5% of breast fed infants unconjugated hyperbilirubinaemia persists beyond the second week and remains unchanged thereafter for between 2 and 16 weeks. The infant is well and thriving and the 'direct reacting' bilirubin is not increased.

This condition is completely benign; if breast feeding is discontinued for 24 to 48h, the bilirubin falls. A similar degree of jaundice occurs in 25% of siblings of affected infants; it appears to be due to factors in maternal milk which inhibit UDP-glucuronyltransferase activity.

PERINATAL INFECTIONS

Neonatal hepatitis may be caused by a variety of viral and bacterial infections (see Table 3.3). They can be acquired *in utero*, during delivery, early in the newborn period from the mother or from blood transfusions. They present as a sick infant with conjugated hyperbilirubinaemia, bilirubinuria, pale stools, and increased plasma activities of liver enzymes, although viral causes of conjugated hyperbilirubinaemia are rare.

Table 3.3   Infections causing neonatal hepatitis

	Times of presentation	Diagnostic test(s)
Transplacental		
Rubella	Day 1	Maternal & infant rubella IgM
Cytomegalovirus	Day 1	Maternal & infant CMV IgM
Toxoplasmosis	Day 1	Maternal & infant Toxoplasmosis IgM
Syphilis	Day 1	Mother sero-positive, infant titre high or rising
Perinatally acquired		
Herpes	1st week	Isolation from vesicles or swabs
Cytomegalovirus	Late	CMV specific IgM or culture
Hepatitis A	Late	Serology
Hepatitis B	Any	Serology
Coxsackie	Any	Coxsackie B antibodies Viral Culture (stool & throat swab)

BILIARY ATRESIA.

Approximately 1 in 10000 babies born in the UK has biliary atresia. Suspicion of the diagnosis should be raised by prolonged jaundice due predominantly to conjugated bilirubin, pale stools and increased urinary bilirubin. Liver enzymes are usually elevated and it may be difficult to distinguish this condition from neonatal hepatitis. Diagnosis is made by visualisation of the biliary tree by ultrasound, radio isotope scans (Technetium–DISIDA [diisopropyliminodiacetic acid]) and liver biopsy. It is very important to make the diagnosis promptly as surgery (Kasai hepato-portoenterostomy procedure) has the best results if performed before eight weeks of age. In spite of numerous publications on the subject, late referral is still occuring with consequent poorer outcome of the surgery.

The other major cause of extrahepatic biliary disease in the neonate is a choledochal cyst which can be diagnosed by ultrasound.

ALPHA₁-ANTITRYPSIN DEFICIENCY

Alpha$_1$-antitrypsin deficiency of either the ZZ or SZ phenotypes may present as prolonged neonatal cholestatic jaundice, although liver disease is by no means an invariable consequence. The incidence is approximately 1 in 2000 births. The presentation is variable; some infants have evidence of only mild liver disease which resolves completely, while others progress rapidly to liver failure and, without liver transplantation, will die. The clinical picture may be undistinguishable from that of biliary atresia. Interpretation of plasma alpha$_1$-antitrypsin concentration is difficult in the newborn because of changing concentrations (see p 193); plasma concentrations *per se* do not allow a definitive diagnosis to be made although a concentration of <1.1g/L during the first four weeks of life is suggestive of a possible deficiency. Phenotyping is required to establish the diagnosis

ALAGILLE SYNDROME.
This syndrome is characterised by cholestasis with a decreased number of intrahepatic bile ducts and various congenital malformations. Hepatomegaly is usually present together with facial dysmorphism and congenital cardiac anomalies. It is very rare with an incidence of approximately 1 in 100000 births, and with equal sex incidence.

DISORDERS OF BILIRUBIN METABOLISM IN THE NEONATE
These are all very rare inherited defects and in the absence of a family history should only be considered after exclusion of the above more common causes.

Crigler-Najjar Syndrome type I
This is due to absence of hepatic bilirubin UDP-glucuronyl transferase. It manifests as severe unconjugated nonhaemolytic hyperbilirubinaemia (>340μmol/L) in the first few days of life. The jaundice is persistent and lifelong phototherapy is required to prevent kernicterus. Liver transplantation has been successful in a handful of cases.

A presumptive diagnosis can be made by the finding of a persistently high plasma unconjugated bilirubin concentration, which does not respond to treatment with phenobarbitone, and normal liver function tests.

Definitive diagnosis can be made by the measurement of glucuronyl transferase in liver tissue after 3-4 months of age and by demonstrating the absence of bilirubin glucuronides in the bile. DNA technology is advancing and prenatal diagnosis is likely to be possible in the future.

Crigler-Najjar Syndrome type II.
This is a milder form of the disease with serum bilirubin usually below 340μmol/L. Although UDP glucuronyl transferase activity is reduced it is not

completely deficient and jaundice can be significantly reduced by phenobarbitone treatment. The family, i.e., parents and sibs, should be investigated for jaundice. Some parents have a mild unconjugated hyperbilirubinaemia with no liver dysfunction (Gilbert's syndrome) and this may represent a heterozygous form of the disease.

Dubin-Johnson and Rotor syndromes.
Presentation of both syndromes is as conjugated hyperbilirubinaemia with normal liver size and plasma liver enzyme activities. The extent of jaundice is enhanced by stress or fasting. Both these disorders are benign with an excellent prognosis. Although the two disorders are phenotypically similar they do differ with respect to urinary porphyrin excretion and bromosulphthalein excretion (see further reading).

OTHER CAUSES OF PROLONGED JAUNDICE.
Galactosaemia and tyrosinaemia type I are discussed in Chapter 6 (see pp 104-113) and hypothyroidism in Chapter 5 (see p 83). Zellweger's syndrome characteristically presents with a combination of hypotonia, jaundice and dysmorphic features (see Ch 6, p 118). Fructosaemia is unlikely to present in the neonate unless a sucrose containing milk formula or medicines have been given. Although cystic fibrosis rarely causes cholestasis, in a few cases biliary obstruction can be severe enough to resemble biliary atresia. G6PD deficiency should be considered in any jaundiced infant of Mediterranean descent.

INVESTIGATION OF JAUNDICE.
Any neonate with prolonged jaundice (i.e., continuing beyond 10 days of age) must be investigated, particularly if there is conjugated hyperbilirubinaemia (Fig 3.3).

The hallmarks of cholestatic jaundice are conjugated hyperbilirubinaemia, pale stools and dark urine. Clinical signs can be helpful in the differential diagnosis. Babies with biliary atresia are usually of normal birth weight and have hepatomegaly without splenomegaly. The baby with an intrauterine infection or an inborn error of metabolism is more likely to be small for dates, to have failed to thrive, have splenomegaly in addition to hepatomegaly and may have dysmorphic features. The definitive diagnosis of a metabolic disorder requires further biochemical investigations (see Table 3.4). These tests should be interpreted in conjunction with historical data, clinical presentation and the results of other investigations, e.g., radiology, virology, haematology and histology.

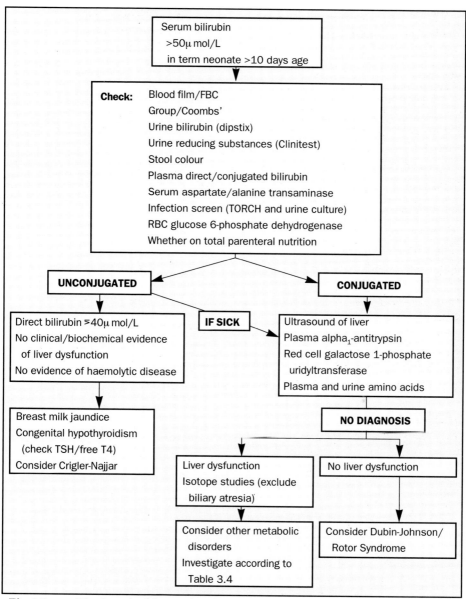

Fig 3.3   Biochemical investigation of prolonged jaundice

Table 3.4   Biochemical Investigation of Patients with Persistent Neonatal Jaundice for Metabolic Disease

BLOOD

• Bilrubin (Total and direct or conjugated)	• Alkaline phosphatase
• Alanine aminotransferase (ALT)	• Gamma-glutamyltransferase
• Albumin	• Cholesterol
• Calcium	• Phosphate
• Sodium	• Potassium
• Creatinine	• Fasting glucose
• Lactate	• Free fatty acids
• Beta-hydroxybutyrate	• Qualitative amino acids
• Thyroid function tests —check that neonatal screening tests have been performed	• Alpha $_1$-antitrypsin
• Galactose 1-phosphate uridyltransferase (qualitative screen)	• Glucose 6-phosphate dehydrogenase —if high risk group check that screening has been performed
• Prothrombin time	• Partial thromboplastin time

URINE

• Amino acids	• Organic acids
• Sugars	

NOTES

1) If plasma amino acids show an increased tyrosine or methionine, second line tests are:
   Plasma alpha-fetoprotein
   Urinary succinylacetone

2) If the baby is acutely ill, consider:
   Ammonia and orotic acid for urea cycle defects and urgent investigations for fatty acid oxidation and glycogen storage disorders.

3) Patients with persistent cholestasis of unknown cause should also be considered for disorders of bile acid synthesis, Zellweger's syndrome, cystic fibrosis and Niemann-Pick type C.

A significant delay in diagnosis/treatment of an infant with cholestasis can be devastating if the erroneous assumption is made that the jaundice is 'physiological' or due to breast feeding. Conjugated hyperbilirubinaemia in the newborn must be investigated.

DISORDERS OF CALCIUM HOMEOSTASIS (see also Chapter 4)

FETAL AND NEONATAL CALCIUM HOMEOSTASIS

Calcium is actively transported to the fetus by the placenta probably via stimulation of membrane ATPase, particularly in the last trimester of pregnancy. Ninety-nine percent of the body pool is in the bony skeleton; it is estimated that intrauterine retention of 3.2mmol/kg/24h of calcium and 2.5mmol/kg of phosphate occurs. Fetal plasma calcium concentration increases from about 1.38mmol/L at 20 weeks to 2.75 mmol/L at term. Fetal plasma total and ionised calcium concentrations are higher than those in the mother due to the active transport across the placenta. It is thought that 1,25-dihydroxycholecalciferol may be involved in this active transport process; the placenta has the capacity to 1-hydroxylate 25-hydroxycholecalciferol.

In the first hours after birth, plasma total and ionised calcium concentrations decrease rapidly to a nadir after 1-2 days, after which there is a slow rise to a constant level which is then maintained (total calcium 2.2 to 2.6 mmol/L). This fall in the perinatal period is associated with transiently low plasma levels of parathyroid hormone. Stress and/or prematurity may prolong this return to normal.

HYPOCALCAEMIA

Biochemical hypocalcaemia can be defined as a total plasma calcium below 1.8mmol/L or an ionised calcium below 0.7mmol/L. Symptomatic hypocalcaemia, which is relatively uncommon, can present as irritability, twitching or convulsions, or as vomiting, poor feeding and lethargy. The QT interval of the ECG is characteristically prolonged.

Causes of Hypocalcaemia (see Table 3.5)

Physiological Hypocalcaemia
Exaggeration of the physiological fall in plasma calcium in the first three days of life leads to a mild, self-limiting disorder. Symptoms are commoner in pre-term

Table 3.5 Causes of neonatal hypocalcaemia

• Physiological	— Prematurity
	— Infants of diabetic mothers
	— Birth asphyxia
• Pathological	— Vitamin D deficiency
	— Hypoparathyroidism
	— Pseudohyperparathyroidism
	— Maternal hypoparathyroidism
	— Liver disease
	— Renal disease
	— Hypomagnesaemia
	— Organic acid disorders
• Iatrogenic:	— Low calcium intake
	— Parenteral nutrition
	— High phosphate intake
	— Diuretics
	— Anticonvulsants
	— Exchange transfusion

infants (see Ch 4), infants of diabetic mothers and, following birth asphyxia. Low concentrations of maternal and fetal 25-hydroxyvitamin D e.g., in Asian or vegan mothers, will pre-dispose the neonate to 'early' hypocalcaemia and are a contributory factor.

Physiological hypoparathyroidism in the neonate probably arises as a result of the relative fetal hypercalcaemia due to the active placental transfer of calcium. Stress may cause release of tissue phosphate and thus depression of calcium, which cannot be corrected in the absence of PTH. This early neonatal hypocalcaemia is often asymptomatic and tends to remit spontaneously after a few days. If it persists then further investigation is warranted.

Hypoparathyroidism.
Primary hypoparathyroidism in the neonate is rare. It can be isolated, with biochemical findings of hyopocalcaemia, hyperphosphataemia, hypomagnesaemia, low or normal alkaline phosphatase and a low or absent plasma immunoreactive PTH. This condition may be genetic in origin, X-linked inheritance being commonest.

Di George's syndrome comprises a similar biochemical picture in association with thymic aplasia and immunodeficiency. Cardiac defects and facial anomalies may also be present.

Transient hypoparathyroidism. Rarer forms of transient hypoparathyroidism, lasting up to one year, have been described, as have cases with biologically inactive PTH and a ring chromosome 16 or 18.

Maternal biochemical disorders e.g., primary hyperparathyroidism, may expose the fetus to chronic hypercalcaemia, and hence may cause fetal parathyroid suppression and apparently unexplained neonatal hypocalcaemia.

Iatrogenic
The condition of 'late' hypocalcaemia is now very rare, presenting as fits between five and seven days of age in previously normal term infants fed unmodified cows milk formulas. The cause was the relatively high phosphate content of these milks. The long term use of anticonvulsants, diuretics or inappropriately supplemented parenteral nutrition can also cause hypocalcaemia. Anticoagulants in transfused blood may also lead to hypocalcaemia.

Apparent hypocalcaemia
Hypoalbuminaemic states, particularly in hydrops fetalis or in the very immature infant, may lead to low total serum calcium but with normal ionised calcium and an absence of symptoms. Treatment is that of the primary condition.

INVESTIGATION OF HYPOCALCAEMIA IN THE NEONATE.
The differential diagnosis of hypocalcaemia should be considered according to Fig 3.4 and Table 3.6. Unexplained, persistent hypocalcaemia in the term baby should be initially investigated as follows :

plasma: phosphate

                   magnesium

                   alkaline phosphatase

                   albumin

                   creatinine

                   acid base status

The mother, particularly if Asian or a vegan, should be investigated for vitamin D deficiency by measurement of plasma 25-hydroxycholecalciferol. Further investigation, including measurement of PTH and 1,25 dihydroxycholecalciferol

Table 3.6 Biochemical findings in neonatal hypocalcaemia

Cause	Presenting Age	Plasma Phosphate	Plasma ALP†	Other Plasma Investigations
Physiological	24h–48h	N	N	
Vitamin D deficiency				
maternal	24h-48h*	N/↓	↑	PTH ↑ /N
1-alphahydroxylasedeficiency	Infancy**			
fat malabsorption	Any			
Hypoparathyroidism	Any**	↑	N	PTH ↓↓
Pseudohypoparathyroidism	Any**	↑	N	PTH ↑ /N
Primary hypomagnesaemia	>5 days	N	N	Mg^{2+} <0.4mmol/L
Iatrogenic	>5 days	N / ↑	N	

†   Alkaline phosphatase [ALP]

*   later if breast feeding   **   rare to present in neonate

may be required. The characteristic biochemical findings in the different causes of hypocalcaemia are shown in Table 3.6

MANAGEMENT OF HYPOCALCAEMIA

Asymptomatic hypocalcaemia requires no treatment. Seizures may respond to slow intravenous injection of 2mL/kg 10% calcium gluconate, followed by oral calcium gluconate supplements 200-500 mg/kg/24h. Secondary hypocalcaemia should be managed by treatment of the underlying disorder.

HYPERCALCAEMIA

This is less common than hypocalcaemia. It is defined as a plasma calcium of >2.75 mmol/L. Clinical irritability, weakness, constipation, failure to thrive, polydipsia, polyuria and nephrocalcinosis with renal failure can all occur.

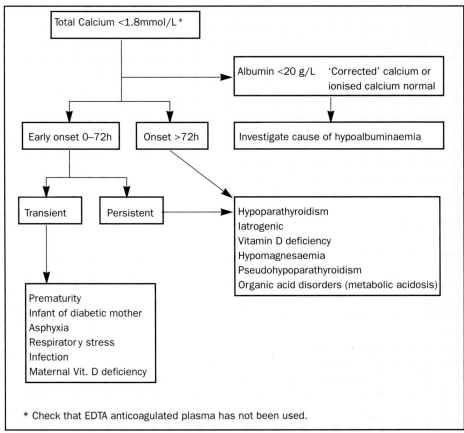

Fig 3.4   Investigation of neonatal hypocalcaemia

William's syndrome is a serious sporadic disorder in which hypercalcaemia is associated with an 'elfin' facies, supravalvar or other aortic stenosis, mental retardation and failure to thrive. Treatment of the hypercalcaemia does not appear to affect the other features of the condition.

Hypercalcaemia associated with hypophosphataemia can occur in the phosphate depleted pre-term infant (see Ch 4, p 72) due to parenteral feeding or unsupplemented breast milk. Excess Vitamin D administration, primary hyperparathyroidism, or the autosomal dominant condition benign familial hypocalciuric hypercalcaemia, can all cause hypercalcaemia in this age group.

PRIMARY HYPOMAGNESAEMIA

Hypomagnesaemia may lead to hypocalcaemia by reducing PTH secretion or reducing responsiveness of the parathyroids to calcium, i.e., PTH concentration may be low or normal. Although it is generally rare in term neonates it is particularly common in infants of diabetic mothers. It may manifest as refractory hypocalcaemia within the first week of life. If plasma magnesium falls below 0.4mmol/L treatment with intramuscular 50% magnesium sulphate 0.2mL/kg should be given.

HYPOGLYCAEMIA

DEFINITION

The definition of 'hypoglycaemia' in the neonate is controversial and has been repeatedly modified. Currently the majority of British paediatricians continue to define hypoglycaemia as a blood glucose concentration of less than 2.0mmol/L in full term infants, or less than 1.1 mmol/L in premature or small for gestational age infants. It is likely, however, that there is a continuum of risk of hypoglycaemia depending on individual factors and that a 'cut off' blood or plasma glucose value is artificial. The most important consequence of low blood glucose is neuroglycopaenia. In animals, severe and prolonged hypoglycaemia leads to cellular energy failure and membrane depolarisation, producing neuronal necrosis. In man, studies relating plasma glucose to specific neurological dysfunctions may lead to a better definition of inadequate blood glucose concentration.

A recent study showed abnormal brainstem somatosensory evoked potentials in neonates at blood glucose concentration between 0.7 and 2.5 mmol/L. In 50%, no clinical changes were noted. All changes were reversed immediately by intravenous glucose. Currently, clinicians concentrate on maintaining generous normoglycaemia in newborn babies to avoid possible neuro-developmental damage.

CLINICAL HYPOGLYCAEMIA

Some neonates tolerate very low blood glucose concentrations without any clinical symptoms, presumably by utilising alternative fuels. Clinical signs attributable to hypoglycaemia include jitteriness, irritability, convulsions or cyanotic/apnoeic attacks, floppiness, poor feeding and coma. These are all non-specific features.

PREVENTION OF HYPOGLYCAEMIA

Most hypoglycaemia occurs during the first 6-12 hours after birth. The frequencyis increased four-fold in low birthweight infants. Particular infants at risk include those with birth asphyxia, infection, smallness for gestational age, maternal diabetes or Rhesus haemolytic disease. Most hospitals screen for hypoglycaemia with a protocol such as that shown in Fig.3.5.

TREATMENT OF HYPOGLYCAEMIA.

Hypoglycaemia suspected from reagent stick testing MUST be confirmed by laboratory glucose measurement. Once the diagnosis is made treatment should follow a schedule such as shown in Fig 3.6. Symptomatic hypoglycaemia, or hypoglycaemia in a baby not tolerating feeds, requires immediate admission to a Neonatal Unit and intravenous dextrose administration. Most hypoglycaemia due to fuel depletion will respond to these measures.

RESISTANT PERSISTENT HYPOGLYCAEMIA.

If hypoglycaemia persists or the baby requires a glucose infusion in excess of 10.0mg/kg/min to maintain a normal plasma concentration, metabolic and endocrine disorders must be considered (see Table 3.7).

SPECIFIC CONDITIONS ASSOCIATED WITH HYPOGLYCAEMIA

SMALL FOR GESTATIONAL AGE (SGA) INFANTS
Those infants who are light for gestation following intrauterine malnutrtion are particularly at risk for hypoglycaemia. This group tend to have well preserved head growth, but absent adipose tissue. They have depleted hepatic glycogen stores and are also thought to have impaired gluconeogenesis despite elevated plasma glucagon, growth hormone and cortisol concentrations. The reason is unclear, but low levels of the enzyme phosphoenolpyruvate carboxykinase (PEPCK) have been documented in growth retarded neonatal animals. Decreased fatty acid oxidation has also been postulated.

A proportion of SGA infants have inappropriately raised plasma insulin concentrations and are at risk of recurrent hypoglycaemia and long term neurological sequelae.

SGA infants should be milk fed as soon as possible after birth, with frequent monitoring of blood glucose. If glucose infusion is needed, weaning onto milk

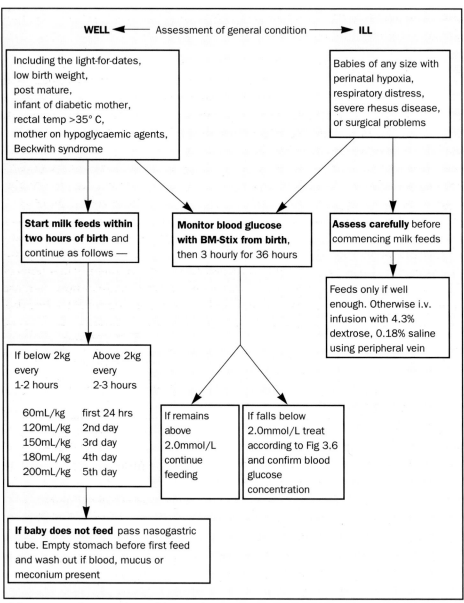

Fig 3.5   Prevention of hypoglycaemia: management of
           neonates 'at risk'

feeds from this can usually be achieved after 2-3 days. Occasionally, very high glucose administration rates are necessary to maintain normoglycaemia.

INFANTS OF DIABETIC MOTHERS

Hyperinsulism in the neonate is inversely related to the adequacy of maternal control of blood glucose in the third trimester. The fetus can be as severely affected in a gestational diabetic as in a mother with established diabetes. If maternal diabetes is recognised, fetal growth will be closely monitored and the mother will usually be treated with insulin. An unexpectedly large infant with early hypoglycaemia may result when the mother has hitherto unrecognised prediabetes. This can be established postnatally by performing a maternal glucose tolerance test at six weeks. Hypoglycaemia can present within an hour of birth. Usually such severely affected infants are large for gestational age. They may have had a traumatic delivery, shoulder dystocia being a particular hazard since the head size is relatively small. Polycythaemia, congenital defects, jaundice, lung immaturity and hypocalcaemia all occur more frequently in infants of the diabetic mother. The majority of infants of diabetic mothers however, are appropriate for gestational age in weight and with early and frequent (2-3hourly)

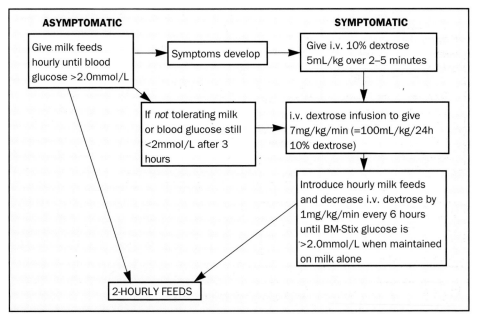

Fig 3.6   Treatment of hypoglycaemia

Table 3.7   Causes of hypoglycaemia in the neonate

Decreased glucose production

Preterm	Antenatal nutritional deficiency	Sepsis	Birth asphyxia
Hypothermia	Small for gestational age	Starvation	Congenital heart disease

Hyperinsulinism

Maternal diabetes	Beckwith syndrome	Nesidioblastosis
Maternal drug therapy or glucose starvation	Erythroblastosis fetalis	Insulinoma

Inborn errors of metabolism

Carnitine deficiency disorders (e.g., carnitine palmityl transferase deficiency)	Glycogen storage disorders, especially type I	Disorders of gluconeogenesis (e.g., pyruvate carboxylase deficiency)
Amino acid disorders (e.g., tyrosinaemia type I)	Organic acid disorders (e.g., methylmalonic acidaemia)	Disorders of fat oxidation (e.g., medium chain acyl CoA dehydrogenase deficiency)
Galactosaemia		

Hormone deficiencies

Congenital hypopituitarism	Congenital glucagon deficiency	Congenital adrenal hyperplasia	Adrenal hypoplasia/insufficiency

Other

Exchange transfusion

feeds from birth and appropriate (3 hourly) monitoring of blood glucose, never become hypoglycaemic. Symptomatic infants or those who become hypoglycaemic despite early feeding require admission to the Neonatal Unit and i.v. dextrose infusion (see Fig. 3.6). Hyperinsulism is the primary cause of their hypoglycaemia, but they may also have failure of the normal increase in plasma glucagon at two hours of age.

NESIDIOBLASTOSIS.

This condition is caused by overgrowth of insulin producing beta cells within the pancreas, either generalised ('adenomatosis') or more rarely as a focal adenoma.

The cells lie outside the islets of Langerhans. Hyperinsulinaemia before birth leads in most cases to physical resemblance to the infant of a poorly controlled diabetic mother at birth, with macrosomia and increased adipose tissue. Severe intractable hypoglycaemia with hyperinsulism is a uniform feature. Most affected infants present with symptomatic hypoglycaemia in the first 72 hours although presentation can be delayed for up to six months. Diagnosis depends on demonstrating an inappropriately high plasma insulin concentration in relation to the blood glucose, although the absolute insulin concentration may not be grossly abnormal. The hypoglycaemia is non-ketotic. A glucose infusion rate of>10mg/kg/min is required to maintain normoglycaemia. The neurological outcome depends on the promptness and adequacy of management of the hypoglycaemia. Where hyperinsulinaemic hypoglycaemia is persistent and severe, urgent surgery (subtotal pancreatectomy) is required, after which the hypoglycaemia is usually very much easier to manage.

The aim of management is to prevent symptomatic hypoglycaemia. Glucose infusion alone, even at very high rates (15- 20mg/kg/min) may be insufficient. Intramuscular glucagon (0.lmg/kg) has a hyperglycaemic effect but this is short-lived. Long-acting glucagon may be a useful medium term measure as may somatostatin and diazoxide with chlorothiazide. Surgery becomes urgent if these measures fail. A localised adenoma may be demonstrable by arteriography of the coeliac axis and its removal will then be curative.

BECKWITH SYNDROME.
This condition is associated with a deletion within the short arm of chromosome 11. Features, some or all of which may be present, include macrosomia, macroglossia, exomphalos, visceromegaly, horizontal creases on the earlobe and hyperinsulinaemic hypoglycaemia. The syndrome can usually be recognised at birth. Hypoglycaemia is a feature in 50% of cases and is associated with islet cell hypertrophy. It may be transient or occasionally persistent for several months and associated with later mental retardation. Screening for neonatal hypoglycaemia is therefore important in infants with any features of this condition. There is an association with renal tumours in later childhood.

INVESTIGATION OF HYPOGLYCAEMIA
There are numerous causes of persistent or recurrent hypoglycaemia, many of them genetic in origin (Table 3.7). Investigations should proceed according to Fig. 3.7. The identification of an associated metabolic acidosis, and/or liver

dysfunction are important in guiding the approach to further investigations (Table 3.8)

COLLECTION OF SAMPLES

In all cases of hypoglycaemia, suggested by a 'stix' test result the accurate blood or plasma glucose must be confirmed by an accurate laboratory test. A BM-Stix result of <2.0 mmol/L is an unreliable result on which to base further investigations. Measurement of metabolites and hormones in plasma and screening for urinary ketones (Acetest) in specimens taken at the same time as hypoglycaemia can provide important diagnostic information. It is therefore of great importance to collect appropriate specimens when the baby is hypoglycaemic. Store urine (5mL ideally, 1-2mL is useful) and plasma (2mL in fluoride ideally) at -20 °C for further investigation.

The extent of investigation may be limited by the small specimen of blood likely to be available and hence must be individualised.

KETONURIA

Ketosis is a normal physiological response to hypoglycaemia, due to production of ketone bodies in the liver (acetoacetate, 3-hydroxybutyrate) from fatty acids released from adipose tissue. *Absence of ketonuria* at the time of severe hypoglycaemia is abnormal and strongly suggests hyperinsulinism or a fat oxidation defect. Ketotic hypoglycaemia points to hormone deficiency or an inborn error of metabolism.

FASTING/FED PROFILE OF METABOLITES.

If hypoglycaemia relates specifically to starvation or feeding, then useful diagnostic information can sometimes be obtained by measuring a variety of metabolites in the fed or fasted states. This approach requires careful planning between the clinician and clinical biochemist so as to maximise data obtained from the precious, usually limited blood specimens. Careful clinical supervision is essential as the risk of hypoglycaemia is obviously great.

Metabolites which are useful to measure include plasma lactate, 3-hydroxybutyrate, free fatty acids and alanine, in addition to glucose.

In the authors' experience pyruvate is not recommended, as current methodologies have limitations and only rarely does the knowledge of the concentration contribute to the diagnosis.

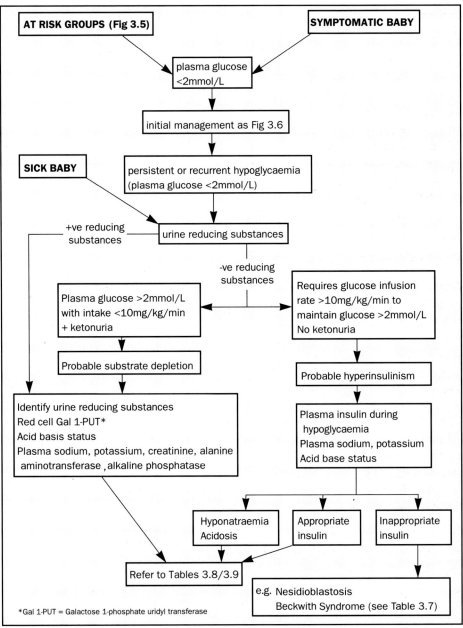

Fig 3.7   Investigation of neonatal hypoglycaemia

A variety of tolerance tests, e.g., glucagon, alanine, galactose have been used to investigate hypoglycaemia. They are not recommended in the neonate and are rarely required in older infants. In most situations the diagnosis of an inborn error of metabolism or hormone defect can be reached by following the protocol outlined (see Fig 3.7).

Table 3.8   Further investigation of neonatal hypoglycaemia

	Further Investigations	**Diagnoses**
Metabolic acidosis	Plasma lactate	Glycogen storage types I
	Plasma 3-hydroxybutyrate	Congenital lactic acidosis
	Plasma free fatty acids	Disorders of gluconeogenesis
	Urine organic acids	Fatty acid oxidation defects
Liver dysfunction	Plasma and urine amino acids	Tyrosinaemia type I
	Galactose 1-phosphate uridyl transferase	Galactosaemia
	Urine sugars	Hereditary fructose intolerance
	Urine organic acids	Fatty acid oxidation effects
Absence of acidosis and liver dysfunction	Plasma cortisol	Adrenal insufficiency
	Plasma 17-hydroxyprogesterone	Adrenal hyperplasia
	Plasma insulin (when hypoglycaemic)	Nesidioblastosis
	Plasma growth hormone and TSH	Hypopituitarism
Hyponatraemia	Plasma 17-hydroxyprogesterone	Adrenal hyperplasia
	Plasma cortisol	Adrenal insufficiency
	Plasma growth hormone and TSH	Hypopituitarism

SODIUM AND POTASSIUM DISTURBANCES
(See also Chapter 4)

INTRODUCTION
The goal of management of fluid and electrolytes in the sick neonate is to maintain balance by ensuring appropriate intake to satisfy normal requirements together with any additional requirements imposed by abnormal losses occuring as a result of disease. Specific factors which need to be taken into account when calculating replacements in the neonate are body composition, insensible water loss from skin and respiratory tract, and the immaturity of the neuroendocrine system and kidneys for controlling water and electrolyte balance.

Body water at term is about 78% of total body weight and just over half is intracellular. In the first few days of life, the extracellular water compartment contracts as a result of increased water excretion by the kidneys associated with improvement of renal function. Failure of this diuresis can precipitate conditions such as congestive cardiac failure due to persistent patent ductus arteriosus, necrotising enterocolitis and the development of bronchopulmonary dysplasia.

Insensible water loss, though mainly of importance in the small, immature infant, may be significantly increased by hyperthermia, use of a radiant over-head baby warmer and use of phototherapy. These latter two can increase losses by 30 to 50% by increasing heat expenditure secondarily to absorption of radiant heat energy. Maintenance of high ambient humidity in incubators and respiratory circuits is an important factor in reducing such losses. These losses are not directly measurable, but their relative importance in the sick infant can be estimated by regular accurate weighing of the baby with electronic scales combined with measurement of urine osmolality. Basal water loss in the term infant approximates to 20mL/kg/24h.

The control of fluid balance involves antidiuretic hormone and mineralocortoids, as in the older child. Although production of these hormones is well established in the neonate, their effect is limited by the relative unresponsiveness of the end organ.

MAINTENANCE REQUIREMENTS
Daily fluid requirements must take account of tissue growth, stool water loss (approximately 10 mL/kg/24h after the first week), insensible water loss, averaging 20 mL/kg/24h, and urinary water loss, which will depend on solute

excretion and urinary concentration. A standard regimen for fluid administration (parenteral or oral) to a well, full term baby would be as follows:

Day 1	60 mL/kg
Day 2	90 mL/kg
Day 3	120 mL/kg
Day 4	150 mL/kg
Day 5	180 mL/kg

Parenteral fluid would normally be given as dextrose with added electrolytes to provide 2-3 mmol/kg/24h of both sodium and potassium, usually with the addition of 1 mmol/kg/24h of 10% calcium gluconate. This is most conveniently achieved by adding supplementary potassium chloride and calcium gluconate to a bag of dextrose saline (which contains 4% dextrose and 0.18% saline). In infants nursed under phototherapy or a radiant warmer, this regime would be increased by 30 mL/kg/24h.

This regime would not be appropriate for infants with perinatal asphyxia, suspected renal impairment or immediately post surgery. In such situations total fluid intake should remain restricted to 40-60 mL/kg/24h until adequate renal function was established. This can be assessed by measurement of plasma creatinine and urine output.

Abnormal losses should be replaced according to their electrolyte composition. The commonest - an increased volume of gastric aspirate - is usually replaced by 0.45% saline i.v. in equivalent volume to that lost, with added potassium chloride to a concentration of 3-4 mmol/L.

CALCULATIONS OF SODIUM DEFICIT IN DEHYDRATION

Where a term infant has become dehydrated, it is possible to calculate the deficit of solute assuming total body water (expected) of 0.7 L/kg and to replace this over 48 hours. Dehydration may be quantified from percentage weight loss with time. If weight loss is unknown, clinical assessment of dehydration must suffice. If a baby is estimated to be more than 10% dehydrated, with loss of skin turgor, sunken fontanelle and peripheral coolness, colloid, (15mL/kg) usually as plasma or 4.5% albumin must be rapidly administered first to restore circulating volume before dextrose/electrolyte replacement is considered. Larger volumes may be required depending on the precise circumstances.

Dehydration can be classified, on the basis of plasma sodium concentration, into isotonic ($[Na^+]$ 130-145 mmol/L), hypotonic ($[Na^+]$ <130 mmol/L), or hypertonic ($[Na^+]$ >145 mmol/L). The latter is uncommon and most likely to be iatrogenic. In hypertonic states, great caution must be exercised in correction of dehydration, as too rapid body fluid expansion can produce convulsions and cause irreversible cerebral damage.

An electrolyte deficit can be calculated from the difference in expected body solute concentration before dehydration and the observed concentration in the dehydrated state:

e.g., in a baby with >10% dehydration, where estimated body water is 0.6L/kg as compared to 0.7L/kg expected value,

$$\text{mmol deficit of solute} = (0.7 \times 280) - (0.6 \times 2 \times \text{plasma } [Na^+])$$

(loss assumed to be 50% sodium, 50% potassium where expected plasma $[Na^+]$ is 140 mmol/L)

Electrolyte replacement is given over 24-48 hours. Care should be taken not to give potassium until a good urinary output is established.

DISTURBANCES IN SODIUM AND POTASSIUM IN TERM INFANTS

Plasma sodium concentration falls slightly in the first few hours after birth, then rises to regain the cord value by 24 hours of age. Plasma potassium falls minimally during the first 72 hours. Plasma chloride remains unchanged. Total protein rises with the contraction of plasma volume during this period. Sodium reabsorption by the kidneys increases rapidly in the first postnatal days. This is thought to be due to aldosterone-mediated maturation of distal tubular function.

HYPO- AND HYPERNATRAEMIA

Hyponatraemia (plasma $[Na^+]$ <130 mmol/L) and hypernatraemia (plasma $[Na^+]$ >145 mmol/L) have a number of possible aetiologies, and should not be assumed simply to be due to deficiency or excess of solute (Tables 3.9 and 3.10). Both disturbances can be associated with neonatal seizures. This may be because of effects on membrane depolarisation in the central nervous system resulting in abnormal electrical phenomena.

Excessive sodium administration is likely to lead to water retention, expansion of the intravascular volume, development of oedema and cardiac failure. Salt depletion, if chronic, has been associated with slowing of postnatal weight gain.

Table 3.9 Disorders causing hyponatraemia

Condition	Aetiology/Presentation	Management
Maternal influence	Reflects maternal electrolytes (seen especially if large volumes dextrose given i.v. during labour)	Nil — recovers
Iatrogenic	Prolonged administration of i.v. dextrose without electrolyte additives	Restrict fluids. Give Na⁺.
Birth injury Meningitis	Inappropriate ADH secretion Poor urine output Weight gain plasma osmolality below 270mmol/kg Urine osmolality increased	Fluid restriction
Diuretic administration (especially loop diuretics)	Loss of electrolyte in excess of water Drug slowly eliminated in neonates (average losses after 1mg/kg frusemide are 28mL/kg water, 3.6mmol/kg Na⁺, 0.3mmol/kg K⁺.	Replace Na⁺ and water Use amiloride
Acute tubular necrosis, renal failure	Increased renal fractional sodium excretion secondary to tubular damage and hyporesponsiveness to aldosterone	Measure sodium losses and replace by oral or intravenous supplements
Salt losing congenital adrenal hyperplasia	Mineralocorticoid deficiency. Males: normal, or pigmented scrotum Females: virilization (variable) Acute illness in 2nd or 3rd week	See text
Cystic fibrosis	Excessive sweat salt loss in high temperatures (rare presentation)	Rehydrate
Renal tubular acidosis	Loss of sodium and bicarbonate in urine	See text

HYPERKALAEMIA
(VENOUS OR ARTERIAL, NOT CAPILLARY, PLASMA [K⁺] >5.5 MMOL/L)

Hyperkalaemia has a number of causes (Table 3.11). Asymptomatic hyperkalaemia with levels of plasma potassium which would be fatal in a adult (up to 11 mmol/L) can be well tolerated in the short term in a neonate. The most important effect of hyperkalaemia is on cardiac rhythm, particularly in the infant with renal failure in whom the potassium imbalance cannot be readily corrected. This effect of hyperkalaemia is potentiated by hypocalcaemia, even of mild degree. Once renal failure is suspected, supplementary potassium must be removed from administered fluids and any hypocalcaemia corrected with calcium supplements. ECG changes include peaked T waves, then widening of the QRS complex, bradyarrhythmias, sine waves and eventually cardiac arrest. Any

Table 3.10 Disorders causing hypernatraemia

Condition	Aetiology/Presentation	Management
Overhead heater	Excessive water loss through skin especially in preterm babies	Heat shield/Increase water administration as 5% dextrose
Iatrogenic	Administration of $NaHCO_3$ to correct metabolic acidosis.	Promote diuresis
	Administration of excessive supplementary salt over a short time period. Use of 10% (or more) dextrose producing glycosuria and osmotic diuresis (especially in preterm babies)	Alter management
Fluid deprivation Starvation	Dehydration Circulatory collapse	Slow correction of electrolyte imbalance after initial administration of colloid to restore circulatory volume
Excess gastrointestinal fluid loss	Dehydration	As above
Nephrogenic diabetes	Failure to thrive Vomiting, constipation, episodic dehydration Persistent polyuria, unresponsive to exogenous ADH	See text

high potassium value obtained from a capillary sample must be repeated on a venous specimen. Asymptomatic hyperkalaemia of >7 mmol/L in a venous specimen in an infant with renal failure may be treated with rectal calcium resonium resin 1 gram per kg. Hyperkalaemia with ECG changes in any neonate should be treated promptly, initially with 10% calcium gluconate given slowly intravenously at a dose of 0.5 mL/kg with ECG monitoring, followed by a glucose and insulin infusion (1g/kg glucose, e.g., 10mL 10% dextrose/kg) mixed with 0.25 units of insulin/kg given intravenously). Any metabolic acidosis should be treated with sodium bicarbonate. In the infant with renal failure, peritoneal dialysis may be needed.

HYPOKALAEMIA
(VENOUS PLASMA [K+] <3.5 MMOL/L)
This can occur secondarily either to neonatal illness or to therapy. The causes are summarised in Table 3.12.

Table 3.11   Disorders causing hyperkalaemia

Condition	Aetiology/Presentation	Management
Fluid deprivation Dehydration	Dehydration, tissue damage dehydration and leakeage from cells	Correct circulating volume and restore perfusion with colloid and crystalloid
Trauma: bruising, fracture, cephalohaematoma, breech delivery, intracranial haemorrhage	Release of potassium from red cell. Treat if >7 mmol/L or symptomatic	Fluid administration, frusemide or resonium
Acute renal failure	Associated with increased plasma creatinine, and oliguria or anuria	May require treatment with rectal resonium resin, peritoneal dialysis or both
Congenital adrenal hyperplasia Adrenocortical insufficiency	Mineralocorticoid deficiency Males: normal, or pigmented scrotum Females: virilzation (variable)	See text (p 55)
Exchange transfusion	Citrate phosphate dextrose stored blood has average potassium concentration 12–15 mmol/L by 7 days, but can be much higher	Avoid use of blood >5 days old

Table 3.12 Disorders causing hypokalaemia

Condition	Aetiology/Presentation	Management
Birth asphyxia	Part of syndrome of inappropiate ADH with decreased plasma osmolality (<270 mmol/kg)	Fluid restriction
Alkalosis	Renal excretion of K^+ in place of H^+; seen in pyloric stenosis, exogenous alkali administration	Correct alkalosis
Drug induced	Use of frusemide; seen to a lesser extent with all diuretics	Supplement or use potassium-sparing diuretics
Renal tubular acidosis	Proximal RTA (males) —defective proximal tubular resorption of bicarbonate. Distal RTA — inability to establish H^+ion gradient in distal tubule	See text (p 56)
Iatrogenic	Use of glucose and insulin	Reconsider treatment

SPECIFIC DISORDERS CAUSING SODIUM AND POTASSIUM DISTURBANCES

CONGENITAL ADRENAL HYPERPLASIA (CAH) SEE Table 3.13

Inherited defects of steroid biosynthesis can present in the neonatal period as hyponatraemia with renal salt loss, hypoglycaemia, ambiguous or pigmented genitalia and/or failure to thrive. The signs and symptoms of the different disorders reflect the biological activities of the hormones whose synthesis is defective, i.e., cortisol, androgens or aldosterone.

The commonest type (which is autosomal recessive) is due to 21-hydroxylase deficiency, with an appoximate worldwide incidence in the region of 1 in 14000 births. Female patients classically present with virilisation, with or without salt loss and males with salt loss. Diagnosis relies on measurement of plasma or blood 17-hydroxyprogesterone (17OHP). This is elevated in the vast majority of patients with CAH. High concentrations of 17OHP occur in 'sick' and/or premature infants without adrenal disease and in these situations care is required in interpretation.

In a baby with salt-losing CAH, there is likely to be severe hyponatraemia; plasma potassium concentration is normal or high. Urinary sodium is paradoxically high. Urgent treatment is required. Blood should be taken for later measurement of 17OHP before commencing treatment with infusion of 0.9% saline in 5-10% dextrose at 150 mL/kg/24h, and immediate i.v. hydrocortisone 50 mg. Once the definitive diagnosis is made, long term treatment with replacement hormones is required. Mineralocorticoid replacement is usually with 9α-fluorohydrocortisone and glucocorticoid replacement with hydrocortisone.

There are many rarer forms of congenital adrenal hyperplasia, some associated with normal concentrations of 17OHP. Some of the enzyme deficiencies and further tests are listed in Table 3.13. Detailed investigation of urinary stained metabolites will be required in most cases.

RENAL TUBULAR ACIDOSIS

This title refers to a group of conditions in which there is impaired acidification of urine. Glomerular filtration rate is usually normal.

Proximal RTA is due to inadequate reabsorption of bicarbonate in the proximal tubule. It predominantly affects males, may occur as an isolated defect or as part of a generalised proximal tubular defect such as cystinosis or Lowe's syndrome.

Table 3.13 Some causes of congenital adrenal hyperplasia

Enzyme Deficiency	Biochemical abnormalities	
	Plasma	Urine*
21-hydroxylase	↑ 17-hydroxyprogesterone	
11 beta-hydroxylase	↑ 11-deoxycortisol	
3 beta-hydroxysteroid	↑ dehydroepiandrosterone	↑ pregnenetriol
17alpha-hydroxylase	↓ testosterone	↑ 17-deoxysteroids ↓ 17-ketosteroids ↓ 17-hydroxysteroids
18-hydroxylase (corticosterone methyl oxidase, Type I)	↑ renin ↓ aldosterone	↓ aldosterone ↓ 18-hydroxycorticosterone
18-dehydroxygenase of 18-hydroxycorticosterone (corticosterone methyl oxidase, Type II)	↑ renin ↓ aldosterone	↓ aldosterone ↑ 18-hydroxycorticosterone

* Urinary steroid profiles by gas chromatography/mass spectrometry are required
to make a definitive diagnosis.

It may also occur as a transient defect associated with acute infection. There is systemic acidosis with high bicarbonate requirement to maintain a normal plasma concentration. There is a low or normal plasma potassium concentration and hyperchloraemia. The urine can be acidified to pH <5.5 during severe systemic acidosis. Treatment consists of administration of very large quantities of sodium and potassium citrate (10-25 mmol/kg/24h). Failure to thrive occurs frequently in this condition.

Distal RTA can be inherited as an autosomal dominant condition. It is due to inadequate excretion of hydrogen ions in the distal tubule. There is characteristically a hypokalaemic metabolic acidosis. In this condition the urine pH does not fall below 6.5 despite systemic acidosis. Fractional excretion of bicarbonate is 5-10 percent during acidosis. Treatment consists of administration of sodium and potassium citrate 1-3 mmol/kg/24h.

NEPHROGENIC DIABETES INSIPIDUS

Onset of this condition is in the neonatal period or early infancy. There is vomiting, constipation, failure to thrive, recurrent fevers, and recurrent episodes of dehydration. Polyuria and polydipsia may not be obvious features. Glomerular filtration rate is usually normal. In episodes of dehydration there is hypernatraemia and hyperchloraemia. Lack of response to exogenous ADH differentiates this condition from pituitary diabetes insipidus. There may be massive urinary tract dilatation (hydronephrosis and hydroureter).

Treatment consists of maintenance of adequate water intake together with use of thiazide diuretics.

GASTROINTESTINAL DISORDERS

Some 'surgical' conditions, e.g., pyloric stenosis, gut atresia and necrotising enterocolitis may lead to a large loss of fluid and electrolytes either externally or into an unavailable 'third space' such as the gut lumen. Significant dehydration, together with peripheral circulatory failure and electrolyte abnormalities may occur. These must be corrected prior to surgery, and in some situations, e.g., established pyloric stenosis with a hypochloraemic hypokalaemic alkalosis, this may take 24-48h of administration of isotonic saline with potassium supplements. A suitable regime is the infusion of 0.9% or 0.45% saline with added potassium chloride in quantity to replace the chloride deficit calculated from the following formula:

$$(100 - \text{measured plasma } [Cl^-]\ (\text{mmol}/L) \times \text{body weight (kg)} = [Cl^-] \text{ deficit (mmol)}.$$

Plasma chloride measurement obviates the need for bicarbonate measurement.

During surgery, calculated fluid and electrolyte requirements should be given in addition to replacement of losses of blood or fluids as they occur. All such losses must be recorded and assessed as accurately as possible.

During the immediate postoperative period, urine flow will be reduced secondarily to increased ADH secretion. Insensible water loss is also likely to be reduced due to decreased skin perfusion. Parenteral fluid intake postoperatively should therefore be reduced to 40 mL/kg/24h with careful monitoring of fluid balance, measurement of plasma and urine sodium and potassium, together with regular assessment of clinical hydration status and monitoring of body weight and urine output.

CYSTIC FIBROSIS

Ten percent of infants with cystic fibrosis (CF) present with meconium ileus. Presenting features are abdominal distension and failure to pass meconium within 48 hours of birth. A family history of CF or neonatal bowel obstruction are suggestive of the diagnosis under such circumstances. All babies with meconium ileus should be investigated for CF by performing a sweat test after four weeks of age.

Measurement of serum or blood spot immunoreactive trypsin (IRT) may be misleading as false negative results can occur in babies with CF if they are investigated following a period where enteral feeding has been withheld, e.g., because of surgery.

More rarely, CF presents as persistent conjugated hyperbilirubinaemia with raised plasma alanine or aspartate aminotransferase activity. The baby may be completely well at this stage and the jaundice may resolve, with failure to thrive and symptoms of pancreatic insufficiency presenting later in infancy. A sweat test should be performed in all babies with unexplained conjugated hyperbilirubinaemia. An even rarer presentation is with hyponatraemia if there has been excessive sweat loss.

RENAL DYSFUNCTION

Renal failure in the neonate is unique in that it occurs after a period of intrauterine life in which most of the renal functions have been performed by the placental circulation. Thus major abnormalities such as renal agenesis may present as an acute problem in the newborn infant. In addition, renal dysfunction occurs in a setting of immature and changing renal function. Glomerular filtration rate (GFR) at birth averages just under 1 mL/kg body weight/min. Postnatally it doubles within the first three weeks of life. The postnatal improvement is thought to be due to increased renal plasma flow with increased blood pressure and redistribution of flow to the renal cortex.

The reserve capacity of the neonatal kidneys to cope with adverse environmental stresses is small. The ability to excrete excessive sodium is limited, probably due to high plasma aldosterone and high distal tubular absorption of sodium. The ability to cope with dehydration is limited by the restricted concentrating ability of the kidney — to a maximal osmolality of about 700mmol/kg. The ability to excrete excess free water is also limited in those situations where ADH is increased, particularly during the acute phase of respiratory distress syndrome and after surgery. The ability to excrete an acid load is limited by the GFR and bymaturity of tubular function.

Renal dysfunction can be due to a congenital abnormality, e.g., renal agenesis. It can be a result of a perinatal disturbance, e.g., birth asphyxia or hypotension, or apost natal incident, e.g., the use of nephrotoxic drugs, septicaemia, shock, dehydration, renal vein thrombosis or surgery — in particular surgery for major congenital heart disease.

DIAGNOSIS OF RENAL DYSFUNCTION

The diagnosis of renal failure depends on the demonstration of increasing plasma creatinine with or without oliguria, generally defined as a urinary flow rate of <0.5 mL/kg/h after the first 24 hours of life. The usual urine flow rate is 1-2 mL/kg/h.

Plasma creatinine concentration at birth is similar to that of the mother. Average plasma creatinine by the second week is 35μmol/L. Acute renal failure is accompanied by a rise in plasma creatinine, consistently by more than 20μmol/L/24 h.

Urinary sodium and potassium concentrations are less useful in assessing the causes of renal failure than in the adult, particularly because of the underlying immaturity of renal tubular sodium handling. Proteinuria, haematuria and microscopy showing red cells or granular casts are all useful pointers to renal damage or disease.

Differentiation of renal disease/damage from prerenal failure due to hypovolaemia is difficult to diagnose biochemically. A fractional excretion of sodium > 3 in a term infant suggests renal disease with lack of tubular capacity to conserve sodium.

Urinary microscopy showing casts and red cells is similarly suggestive of renal disease. Clinical history and examination of the baby are as reliable as laboratory markers in assessing the likelihood of hypovolaemic or hypotensive insults as a cause of renal dysfunction.

MANAGEMENT OF RENAL DYSFUNCTION

The ultimate management option for progressive neonatal renal disease is dialysis, usually peritoneal dialysis. Standard dialysis solutions present difficulties because of neonatal intolerance of large glucose loads in concentrating solutions and slow metabolism of the lactate in the solutions. Continuous arteriovenous haemofiltration is a recently developed alternative. The indications for dialysis in a neonate with a potentially reversible renal problem are fluid overload, severe acidosis, hyperkalaemia (particularly with arrhythmias), and progressively rising plasma creatinine concentration.

Early suspicion of a renal problem together with meticulous attention to fluid and electrolyte balance may frequently avert the need for dialysis in the neonate with peri- or postnatally induced renal dysfunction. Abdominal ultrasound to identify any structural anomaly and bladder catheterisation, to allow measurement of urine flow rate, should be performed early. Response to a fluid challenge of 10 mL/kg of 0.9% sodium chloride solution over one hour should indicate whether there is a prerenal component. Frusemide (1 mg/kg) repeated as necessary, and fluid restriction to a level covering losses, should be instituted. These are likely to be about 50 mL/kg/24h plus any losses from urine and GI tract. Potassium-free intravenous or oral fuids should be given in the acutephase. Acidosis with a base deficit of minus ten or more is usually corrected using sodium bicarbonate to half correct the base deficit (BD) using the formula:

$$(BD \times 0.5 \times 0.3 \times body\ wt\ (kg)) = mmol\ of\ NaHCO_3\ to\ be\ infused$$

The infusion is usually given using 4.2% $NaHCO_3$ over 1-2 h.

There is a significant danger of hypoglycaemia and malnutrition during renal failure and parenteral nutrition may be required if the illness is prolonged. It is important to maintain satisfactory plasma concentrations of calcium and magnesium because of the arrhythmogenicity of hyperkalaemia in the presence of hypocalaemia or hypomagnesaemia. Drugs excreted by the kidney will need to have doses and dosage frequency adjusted and plasma concentrations monitored. Potentially nephrotoxic drugs may have to be discontinued.

The prognosis of renal failure reflects the underlying cause. It should be remembered that ischaemia to other organs, particularly the brain, may produce permanent consequences despite resolution of the renal problem. Up to forty percent of survivors may have persisting decreased creatinine clearance and others may have residual concentrating defects or renal tubular acidosis.

FURTHER READING

Jaundice

Chowdhury JR, Wolkoff AW, Arias IM. Hereditary jaundice and disorders of bilirubin metabolism in: Scriver CR, Baudet AL, Sly WS, Valle D, editors. The Metabolic Basis of Inherited Diseases, New York. McGraw 1989.

Haber BA, Lake AM. Cholestatic jaundice in the newborn. Clin Perinatol 1990; **17**: 483-506.

Newman TB, Haisels HJ. Evaluation and treatment of jaundice in the term infant; a kinder gentler approach. Pediatrics 1992; **89**: 809-818.

Hypoglycaemia

Aynsley-Green A. Hypoglycaemia, Recent Advances in Pediatrics 1992; **10**: 37-62.

Bonham JR. The investigation of hypoglycaemia during childhood. Ann Clin Bioch; **30**: 238-247.

Brain Damage by Neonatal Hypoglycaemia. Lancet (editorial) 1989; i: 882-883.

Collins JE, Leonard JV, Teale D, Marks V, Williams DM, Kennedy CR, Hall MA. Hyperinsulinaemic hypoglycaemia in small for dates babies. Arch Dis Child 1990; **65**: 1118-1120.

Cornblath M, Schwartz R, Aynsley-Green, Lloyd JK. Hypoglycaemia in infancy: The need for a rational definition. Pediatrics 1990; **85**: 834-837.

Renal Function

Brocklebank JT. Renal failure in the newborn. Arch Dis Child 1988; **63**: 991-994.

Coulthard MG. Maturation of glomerular filtration in pre-term and mature babies. Early Hum Dev 1985; **11**: 281-292.

Haycock GB, Aperia A. Salt and the newborn kidney. Paediatr Nephrol 1991; **5**: 65-70.

Calcium

Knisek K. Disorders of calcium and bone metabolism in: Brook CGD, editor. Clinical Paediatric Endocrinology. Blackwell Scientific Publications, Oxford, 1987.

Chapter 4

The Pre-term Infant — Clinical and Biochemical Problems

INTRODUCTION

The average pregnancy lasts 37 - 42 weeks from the date of the last menstrual period. Babies born before the end of the 37th week are known as 'pre-term'. Viable infants may, however, be born as early as 24 weeks gestation (Fig 4.1). The problems of these extremely immature infants are very much greater than those of the near-term baby.

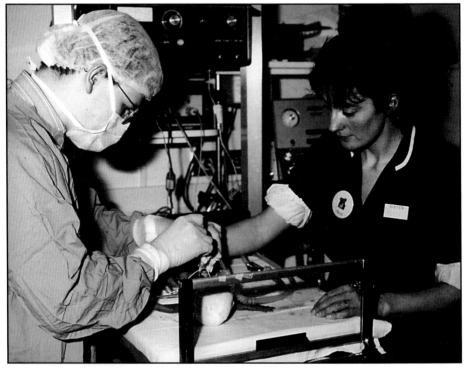

Figure 4.1 Pre-term infant, 24 weeks gestation

Table 4.1   Aetiology of premature birth

- Spontaneous onset of preterm labour
- Preterm rupture of membranes
- Ante partum haemorrhage
- Multiple pregnancy
- Intrauterine infection
- Maternal infection
- Early delivery of baby for maternal reasons:
  - — pre-eclampsia
  - — pregnancy induced hypertension
  - — eclampsia (fits)
  - — cardiac disease
  - — diabetes
  - — other systemic diseases made worse by pregnancy
- Early delivery of baby for fetal reasons:
  - — intrauterine growth retardation
  - — fetal anomaly
  - — fetal distress
  - — deteriorating fetal condition (monitored by ultra sound activity, amniotic fluid volume, Doppler studies)

At any gestational age the baby may also suffer from the consequences of an adverse intrauterine environment and be 'growth retarded'. Commonly, these babies have a weight below the 10th centile for gestation and are defined as 'small for gestational age' (SGA).

Multiple pregnancies are more likely to produce premature babies, the average gestation at birth being 37 weeks for twins and 33 weeks for triplets. Other aetiologies are summarised in Table 4.1.

The complications of prematurity stem from adverse intrauterine or perinatal environment, physical size, or immaturity of body systems (Table 4.2).

Table 4.2 Complications of prematurity

Conditions	Origin	Management
Anaemia	Venepunctures Bone marrow refractory Increasing blood volume with growth Iron deficiency	Replace venesected blood
Bronchopulmonary dysplasia	Complicates RDS in extreme pre-term Prolonged requirement for oxygen	Monitor PO_2 Nutritional support Close monitoring of bacteriological and cardiac status (see also Ch 9)
Hypernatraemia	Common in first 2–3 days in extremely preterm Dehydration	Adequate fluid intake
Hyponatraemia	Renal tubular immaturity (see Table 3.9)	Monitor sodium loss Adequate replacement (up to 10mmol/kg/24h)
Hypocalcaemia	Immature regulation Low plasma albumin	None if asymptomatic Replace in IV fluids if required
Hypoglycaemia	Inadequate intake Low glycogen stores	i.v. dextrose Monitor BM Stix
Hypothermia	Large surface area Immature skin Immature regulation	Clothing Warm environment ± added humidity (incubator usually needed if BW<1.5kg)
Infections (any)	Low immunoglobulins Ineffective localisation of septic foci Invasive treatment	High index of suspicion Early parenteral antibiotics
Intraventricular haemorrhage	Immaturity Cerebro-vascular instablity Post-asphyxia	None possible Rarely progresses to give hydrocephalus
Irregular respiration Apnoea	Immature respiratory centre Infection Intrancranial haemorrhage	Monitor respiration and seek pathological causes Caffeine, theophylline therapy
Jaundice	Delayed food intake Bruising Hepatic immaturity	Phototherapy Exchange transfusion (see Ch 3)
Metabolic acidosis (mild)	Renal immaturity in presence of protein load (milk or TPN)	Reduce protein intake if deteriorating
Necrotising enterocolitis	Infarction of gut secondary to inadequate perfusion	Supportive medical or surgical resection
Osteopenia of prematurity	Progressive demineralisation of bones if mineral absorption inadequate	Mineral supplements to diet
Periventricular leucomalacia	Infarction of large areas of cerebral white matter after ischaemic insult	None possible
Persistent patent ductus arteriosus	Immaturity Hypoxia Acidosis	Ligation or indomethacin Diuretics for heart failure
Respiratory distress syndrome (RDS)	Surfactant deficiency (see Ch 2)	Monitor blood gases Increase inspired PO_2 CPAP or IPPV* i.v. fluids/feeding Exogenous surfactant
Unable to suck reliably	Immature suck/swallow co-ordination	Nasogastric tube feeding if well

*CPAP: Continuous positive airways pressure   IPPV: Intermittent positive pressure ventilation

INTRAUTERINE ENVIRONMENT

Poor transfer of nutrients from placenta to fetus, from whatever cause, leads eventually to intrauterine growth retardation. Affected infants are thin, with antenatally a reduced ratio of abdominal circumference to head circumference, and postnatally a 'scraggy' appearance with little or apparently no fat, and usually a weight and length on a lower centile than that for head circumference. This discrepancy is because brain growth is thought to be preferentially preserved for as long as possible in these circumstances. Such infants may be born at term, or they may be electively delivered early as they are at risk of sudden death *in utero*.

In utero, fetal blood may have low PO_2 because of placental dysfunction so the effects of intrauterine hypoxia may compound those of malnutrition. In the extremely compromised fetus, blood is preferentially directed to the cerebral and cardiac circulations and away from the splanchnic and renal circulations. Such babies will be at risk of developing renal dysfunction (acute tubular necrosis) or gut dysfunction (necrotising enterocolitis) after birth.

Growth retarded infants are particularly at risk of asphyxia at delivery, as the effects of uterine contractions during labour may further compromise their oxygen supply. As well as acute asphyxia, they may show the effects of more chronic hypoxia. Consequences include liver dysfunction with low plasma albumin, low fibrinogen and other liver dependent coagulation factors.

In the long term, this group are at increased risk of developing spastic diplegia, a form of cerebral palsy. The reason for this is unknown, but theories include hypoxia of the developing brain and deficiencies of specific nutrients.

Perinatal mortality associated with premature deliveries could potentially be improved with more aggressive treatment to the fetus. It would be useful therefore if a biochemical marker could be found to identify potential premature delivery. One such potential marker is fetal fibronectin, a protein found in placental tissue and amniotic fluid. Detection of this protein e.g., from vaginal swabs, could serve as a screening test for true pre-term labour and allow informed intervention aimed at improving the outcome.

PERINATAL ENVIRONMENT

Perinatal asphyxia is more common in the pre-term infant than in infants born at full term. Cardiotocographic abnormalities during labour, particularly if the baby is known to be growth retarded, result in a high incidence of delivery by caesarean section. Antenatal monitoring of at risk pregnancies has led to early delivery of a group of babies whose health is deteriorating, or whose mother's health is at risk. In the regional Neonatal Unit in Birmingham, 50% of all admissions have been delivered by caesarean section.

Vigorous attempts are made by obstetric and neonatal staff to avoid perinatal asphyxia. Its consequences include early neonatal hypoglycaemia, inhibition of surfactant production and hence increased severity of respiratory distress syndrome, and impaired regulation of cerebral blood flow. This latter problem produces an increased risk of cerebral haemorrhage (intraventricular haemorrhage) in asphyxiated pre-term babies.

Resuscitation requires the presence of a paediatrician at the delivery of any pre-term infant. The infant must be immediately dried and kept warm with dry towels under a radiant heater. If the baby does not readily establish spontaneous respiration, he will be quickly intubated and ventilated. Small babies who make respiratory efforts but have early evidence of 'stiff' lungs (cyanosis, marked sternal and intercostal recession) also require intubation and positive pressure inflation of the lungs. The baby is then rapidly transferred to the Neonatal Unit after receiving parenteral vitamin K and being shown briefly to the parents. Avoidance of hypothermia is a major priority as hypothermia will lead to inhibition of surfactant production and also to hypoglycaemia.

POSTNATAL CARE

On admission, the pre-term infant is accurately weighed, measured and blood glucose and temperature checked. The baby is placed in a suitable warm environment. This may be a humidified double-walled incubator in a warm (30°C) room for the smallest infants. Overhead radiant heaters may be used during initial assessment. A healthy 1.5 kg baby (i.e., one who does not need to be closely observed and can therefore be fully dressed and wrapped in blankets) will maintain body temperature in a cot in a room environment of 25°C, the average temperature of the low dependency area of a Neonatal Unit. Heat loss can be reduced even in the sickest babies by covering the parts of the body not requiring close observation (e.g., with hats or boots).

Suitable monitoring is then instituted depending on the size, gestation anddependency of the baby. Any respiratory difficulty will preclude early nasogastric feeding, so intravenous or intra-arterial fluids will be required. If the baby requires ventilation, or has an oxygen requirement of >30%, an arterial line is usually inserted (see Ch 9), together with continuous monitoring of oxygenation by TcPO$_2$ (transcutaneous PO$_2$) or SaO$_2$ (oxygen saturation). Intravenous fluids or drugs are given via a peripheral cannula in a hand or foot.

The commonest reason for respiratory support (by headbox oxygen, continuous positive pressure oxygen, or intermittent or triggered positive pressure ventilation) is surfactant deficiency (infantile respiratory distress syndrome, IRDS). This condition is most acute for the first 48-72 hours after which pulmonary compliance improves and the support needed rapidly decreases. Exogenous surfactant, given on the first day of life, can reduce the support required but does not provide a 'cure'.

Small, frail babies will require more nutritional support than can be given orally during this period. Some milk can be given from the second or third day, but this is commonly supplemented by parenteral nutrition from day three or four, given through a long, percutaneously inserted, silastic intravenous catheter (see Ch 8). The baby is at risk of a number of specific problems (Table 4.2) which may require specific intervention.

His maturation (gestational age + postnatal age) will permit the reduction of physiological monitoring with time, lengthening of the interval between feeds, introduction of sucked feeds, and increasing participation by his parents in his care. As he grows and tolerates a lower ambient temperature, he will progress from incubator to cot, and towards the cooler, low-dependency area of the nursery. By a (gestation + postnatal) age of 36 weeks and a weight of about 1.8 kg, he may be ready to be discharged home.

LABORATORY MONITORING

Low birth weight in itself does not produce an increased requirement for laboratory monitoring. This need relates primarily to dependency level and secondarily to maturity. (see Table 4.3).

Table 4.3 Laboratory monitoring related to baby care category

Laboratory Investigations		Baby care category				
		A	B	C$_{(i)}$	C$_{(ii)}$	D
Plasma	Bilirubin (total)	1	4	4	4	4
	Bilirubin (direct)	1	4	4	4	4
	Sodium	1	1	1	2	3
	Potassium	1	1	1	2	3
	Calcium	1	1	1	2	3
	Phosphate	3	3	3	3	4
	Creatinine	1	1	1	2	3
	Albumin	1	1	2	3	4
	Aspartate aminotransferase	4	4	4	4	4
	Alkaline phosphatase	3	3	3	3	4
Blood	Glucose	4	4	4	4	4
	Full blood count	1	2	2	3	3
	Coagulation indices	4	4	4	4	4
Urine	Sodium	1	1	2	3	3
	Potassium	1	1	2	3	3
	Osmolality	4	4	4	4	4
	Creatinine	1	1	2	3	3
	Fractional excretion of sodium (see Ch 2)	1	1	2	3	3
Drugs	Gentamicin pre/post	4	4	4	4	4
	Chloramphenicol pre/post	4	4	4	4	4
	Caffeine	4	4	4	4	4

Key

Frequency of test   1   Daily (or more often)
                    2   Twice weekly
                    3   Weekly
                    4   If relevant (e.g., glucose quantitative if screening BM Stix abnormal or if symptomatic)

Category of Baby (see Table 1.2)

A   **Intensive Care Level I (all gestations)**
    Blood gas analysis (near patient analysis) will also be required at least four hourly for ventilator dependent patients or unstable oxygen dependent patients. TPN monitoring (see Ch 8).

B   **Intensive Care Level II (<30 weeks gestation)**
    Blood gas analysis as above. TPN monitoring (see Ch 8).

C   **Intensive Care Level II (>30 weeks gestation)**
    (i)   On IV Fluids or parenteral nutrition; blood gas analysis as above. TPN monitoring (see Ch 8)
    (ii) On predominantly oral feeds

D   **Special Care Babies**

SPECIFIC PROBLEMS

JAUNDICE (see also Chapter 3)

The aetiological factors for jaundice in the pre-term population include all those found at term, compounded by the increased liver immaturity, more frequent bruising and delayed establishment of enteral feeding in this group. Polycythaemia caused by delayed clamping of the umbilical cord or associated with intrauterine growth retardation may also be seen. The effects of unconjugated bilirubin in the brain are thought to be more dangerous in the pre-term infant than at term. There is reduced albumin binding of bilirubin due to relative hypoproteinaemia; acidosis or hypoxia may reduce the effectiveness of the physiological blood-brain barrier, and the immature brain may itself be more vulnerable to bilirubin toxicity.

For these reasons, the plasma concentrations of bilirubin at which phototherapy or exchange transfusion are employed are lower than those for term infants in most units. Formulae utilised in many UK units are as follows (in non-haemolytic jaundice):

Threshold plasma bilirubin concentration (μmol/L)

— for phototherapy: [gestational age (weeks) $\times$ 10] – 100

— for exchange transfusion: [gestational age (weeks)] $\times$ 10

Physiological jaundice is commonly prolonged beyond ten days in the pre-term population. In our unit we would not investigate prolonged jaundice in a well pre-term baby until the age of 14 days, when we would check plasma total and direct-reacting bilirubin and aspartate aminotransferase (AST), urinary bilirubin, and send urine for culture and reducing substances.

CALCIUM AND PHOSPHATE

PHYSIOLOGICAL HYPOCALCAEMIA (SEE ALSO CHAPTER 3)

Fetal plasma total and ionised calcium, and phosphate concentrations are higher than those in the mother because of active placental transport. Fetal 25-hydroxyvitamin D (25-OHD) concentrations correlate with those of the mother although absolute concentrations are lower. 1,25-dihydroxyvitamin D (1,25-$(OH)_2D$) is not thought to cross the placenta easily and is synthesised both in the placenta and in the fetal kidney. Parathyroid hormone (PTH) and calcitonin do not cross the placenta and are produced by the fetus.

Antenatally, fetal PTH and 1,25-$(OH)_2D$ synthesis are suppressed but calcitonin secretion is increased. This is thought to facilitate the massive increase in fetal bone mineralisation which occurs in the third trimester.

Intrauterine accretion rates by 28 weeks of gestation are approximately 3.0mmol/kg/24h of calcium and 2.0mmol/kg/24h of phosphorus, and this increases steadily up to term.

After birth, total and ionised calcium concentrations fall to a minimum at about 48 hours of age. This fall is more profound in immature infants. The cause is thought to be transient parathyroid suppression secondary to fetal hypercalcaemia. Plasma PTH concentration increases rapidly after the first two days, and hydroxylation of oral vitamin D is possible even in the most immature infants. Although the physiological postnatal rise in plasma 1,25-$(OH)_2D$ is delayed in the pre-term infant, symptomatic hypocalcaemia is rare in this group and seldom causes problems. At Birmingham Maternity Hospital we routinely supplement intravenous fluids for pre-term infants after the first 24 hours with the equivalent of 1 mmol/kg/24h (4.4 mL/kg of 10% solution) calcium gluconate. By 72 hours of age, physiological hypocalcaemia has usually resolved.

RICKETS OF PREMATURITY

Rickets has been recognised as a clinical complication of prematurity for over 40 years. Affected babies are normal at birth, and bony changes develop over the first 6-12 weeks. Typically X-ray changes of osteopenia, flaring and cupping of the bone ends, and fractures can be seen. Clinically, babies show a fall off in longitudinal growth. They can have very mobile rib cages with prominent costochondral junctions, and prolonged oxygen dependency due to increased chest wall compliance. The fractures can be misdiagnosed as being due to nonaccidental injury.

Babies of less than 1500g birth weight used to be particularly at risk of developing this condition. The incidence has diminished significantly in recent years with greater awareness of the specific nutritional needs of smaller babies.

Subclinical bone abnormality in the form of significant demineralisation (which may not be diagnosable on X-ray) can be detected by dual beam photon absorptiometry (available as a research tool in some centres). Using this technique, osteopenia has been reported in 50% of infants weighing less than 1 kg at birth.

The underlying cause of this osteopenia is thought to be a failure to continue the intrauterine rates of calcium and phosphorus accretion once the baby is born, due largely to dietary mineral deficiency. Human breast milk provides the equivalent of 1.4 mmol/kg/24h of calcium and 0.9 mmol/kg/24h of phosphorus in the enterally fed baby. It is likely that only about 65% of the calcium in human milk is absorbed, while the absorbtion from ordinary formula milk is only about 40%. Phosphate is well absorbed from human milk (90%) but poorly (25%) from ordinary formula milk.

The initial abnormality produced will be demineralisation (osteopenia of prematurity), that is a reduced bone mass due to a decrease in the rate of osteoid synthesis. Later, a ricketic phase of bone growth will follow with failure of adequate mineralisation of the bone matrix in growing bone, accumulation of osteoid tissue and development of typical radiological changes.

Biochemical findings usually include a grossly raised plasma total alkaline phosphatase activity (> 1000 IU/L), plasma phosphate concentration low or low normal (<1 mmol/L) and a low urine phosphate/creatinine ratio. Plasma calcium concentration is usually normal but can occasionally be low or even high. In some very small infants in whom plasma phosphate is low, secondary hypercalciuria can occur, together with active demineralisation of bone.

One study of osteopenic low birth weight infants has correlated abnormal placental histology with later development of osteopenia, a low plasma phosphate concentration, maximal percentage tubular reabsorption of phosphate, and high urine calcium excretion. The healthy placenta actively pumps minerals to the fetus. These infants may well therefore have a prenatal phosphate deficiency which in the absence of later adequate dietary phosphate, leads to osteopenia.

PREVENTION OF OSTEOPENIA
Both vitamin D deficiency and mineral depletion can lead to bone demineralisation, maximal at 6 to 12 weeks of age, in pre-term infants. The bone mineralisation will gradually and spontaneously improve thereafter as dietary intake of minerals increases and the rate of bone growth becomes relatively slower. This can be hastened with dietary supplements.

In osteopenic pre-term infants, plasma 25-OHD concentrations are usually normal; plasma 1,25-$(OH)_2$D may be raised. In a minority of studies, however, plasma 1,25-$(OH)_2$D has been found to be low and this has been postulated to be due to a delay in maturation of 1α-hydroxylase. The severity of osteopenia can be reduced in such cases by supplementation with 1,25-$(OH)_2$D.

Vitamin D prophylaxis in the pre-term population has not had a major effect on the incidence of osteopenia of prematurity, and deficiency of 1,25-$(OH)_2$D is not thought to be the major aetiological factor. In practice, 400 IU to 1000 IU per day of Vitamin D is generally recommended for all pre-term infants from the age of seven days until approximately the equivalent of 40 weeks gestation, and should be sufficient to overcome any deficiency of 1α-hydroxylase. It is particularly important that this is given to Asian babies as this community has a high incidence of maternal vitamin D deficiency and the babies are particularly at risk.

More important than vitamin D, is supplementation of diet with calcium and phosphate. This has been shown in a number of studies to reverse the demineralisation seen by photon absorptiometry. Unsupplemented human breastmilk is inadequate for the pre-term infant. Phosphate supplementation alone may cause a rapid fall in calcium concentration in some infants leading to symptomatic hypocalcaemia. Supplementation of human milk with calcium and phosphate is therefore recommended. Disodium phosphate, as buffered neutral phosphate (Joules solution) is recommended and can be given either alone or in the milk in a dose to increase the concentration of phosphate in breast milk from 0.5 to 1.0mmol/100mL. Separate oral doses of calcium gluconate should also be given (1mmol/kg/day).

Newer pre-term formula feeds offer more satisfactory quantities of mineral, the phosphate concentration being approximately double that of expressed breast milk and that of calcium also higher. In a baby on full volume feeds, supplementation should result in a phosphate retention rate of 1.6–1.7mmol/kg/24h compared to <0.1 to 0.9mmol/kg/24h in an infant fed unsupplemented breast milk. Osteopenia is very uncommon in babies fed on pre-term formula milks.

In the sick parenterally fed infant it is important to ensure that calcium and phosphate are administered to the maximal level consistent with solubility. A maximum, of about 1.5mmol/kg/24h of calcium and 1.1mmol/kg/24h of phosphate can be administered. Calcium and phosphate concentrations, and alkaline phosphatase activity in plasma, should be monitored weekly.

ALKALINE PHOSPHATASE ACTIVITY
Plasma alkaline phosphatase activities above the level of normal term infants are common in pre-term low birth weight infants. A value up to double the upper limit of the term neonate reference range may be normal for pre-term infants. Very elevated levels (>1600 IU/L) however may be a marker for osteopenia.

The placental isoenzyme disappears from plasma with a half life of 3–4days. The fetal intestinal isoenzyme may comprise up to 50% of the total plasma alkaline phosphatase within the first month of life. By the end of the sixth postnatal week, when clinical rickets may become apparent, the fetal intestinal isoenzyme makes a negligible contribution to total enzyme activity.

In practice, alkaline phosphatase is measured weekly from the age of 14 days in the at-risk very low birth weight population. A level of >7.5 × upper reference limit is very suggestive of osteopenia.

NEPHROCALCINOSIS
The relatively poor acidification of urine of which the pre-term neonate is capable may lead to calcification within the kidney in the presence of hypercalciuria. This nephrocalcinosis is increasingly recognised as a complication of long term frusemide administration in neonates with congenital heart disease or heart failure secondary to bronchopulmonary dysplasia. Such infants should be screened by regular renal ultrasound. If abnormal calcification is suspected, frusemide should be discontinued and replaced by a thiazide.

TEMPERATURE CONTROL AND WATER BALANCE
The physically smaller pre-term infant has a greater surface area to body weight ratio in comparison with the term baby. The ability to shiver or adopt a flexed position to retain heat is also limited. Active measures to avoid hypothermia must include drying the infant's skin immediately after delivery, use of an efficient radiant heat source during resuscitation, clothing, and a constantly warm thermally neutral environment. For babies <1.5kg birth weight, incubator care is almost always required.

In the extremely pre-term neonate (<30weeks) skin immaturity can lead to massive transudation of water which evaporates, leading to loss of energy as heat. The baby can become dehydrated and cold. This can be minimised by providing a warm, humid environment during the first 48 to 72 hours, after which the skin's function as a waterproof barrier improves considerably.

Fluid administration may need to be markedly increased if large insensible losses are suspected. The baby will develop increased weight loss, high urine osmolality, hypernatraemia, an increasing plasma creatinine and, if severe, clinical signs of dehydration or shock. Up to 100 mL/kg/24h extra crystalloid may need to be given for the first 48 to 72h and plasma sodium, potassium and creatinine concentrations should be closely monitored.

RENAL IMMATURITY

Renal tubular immaturity in the pre-term neonate, together with the low GFR (Table 4.4) lead to a number of practical problems in management. Low creatinine clearance leads to extremely prolonged half-life for many renally excreted drugs e.g., gentamicin. The need for long dosage intervals and the monitoring of plasma drug concentrations has led to altered practice and the use of alternative, non-renally excreted antibiotics in many Neonatal Units.

Tubular leakiness, particularly of sodium, may lead to high urinary sodium losses and hyponatraemia unless a milk with a high sodium content is used e.g., pre-term formulations or breast milk supplemented with salt. Unsupplemented breast milk in a volume of 150 mL/kg/24h will supply only 1–2mmol/kg sodium/24h to the baby.

Table 4.4 Creatinine clearance in neonates measured in first 48 hours of life

Gestational age (weeks)	Creatinine clearance (ml/min) mean ± 1 SD
28	0.35 ± 0.22
30	0.45 ± 0.25
32	0.50 ± 0.20
34	0.46 ± 0.34
36	1.21 ± 0.55
40	2.24 ± 1.58

This amount is inadequate to maintain salt balance until the baby reaches the equivalent of about 34 weeks gestational age. Before this time, salt can be added to milk or given intermittently as medication 4-6 hourly, in sufficient quantity to boost salt intake to 3-4mmol/kg/24h. In our Neonatal Unit, this is done by adding 0.6 mmol NaCl (as 0.6 mL of 1mmol/mL solution) to each 30mL expressed breast milk prior to feeding. For some babies, even this will be insufficient and the urine Na:K molar ratio will fall below one. In these individuals, as in those with increased salt losses (e.g., due to the use of diuretics), salt intake should be boosted until the urine Na:K ratio is greater than one. This may require intakes of 10mmol/kg/24h or more.

ALBUMIN

Hypoproteinaemia is seen in pre-term infants due to decreased hepatic protein synthesis, as well as in sick, term infants and in hydrops fetalis. The correlation of plasma albumin concentration with peripheral oedema is poor in the pre-term population. Poor muscle tone, inactivity, the use of paralysing drugs, fluid overload, or nursing head uppermost, may all contribute to local or general peripheral oedema. Albumin administration, although frequently used in practice is probably inappropriate when prescribed purely to treat this physical finding.

However, albumin administration does produce acute physiological effects of improved perfusion, enhanced urinary output and increased blood pressure dueto enhanced intravascular volume consequent on the effect on plasma oncotic pressure. Albumin administration is useful if it is suspected that the circulating volume might be depleted. Albumin solution (4.5%) is given at a rate of 10–20mL/kg over 1 – 4h. Biochemical (usually nutritional) hypoproteinaemia can also be corrected by infusion of albumin solution. In our Neonatal Unit, 20% albumin solution is given when the plasma albumin falls below 25g/L, using the formula given below as a guide to the amount to be infused.

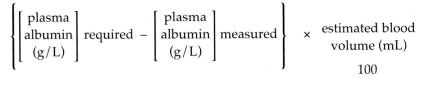

$$\left\{ \begin{bmatrix} \text{plasma} \\ \text{albumin} \\ \text{(g/L)} \end{bmatrix} \text{required} - \begin{bmatrix} \text{plasma} \\ \text{albumin} \\ \text{(g/L)} \end{bmatrix} \text{measured} \right\} \times \frac{\text{estimated blood volume (mL)}}{100}$$

=mL of 20% albumin to be administrated

FURTHER READING

Al-Dahan J, Haycock GB, Chantler C, Stimmler L. Sodium homeostasis in term and pre-term neonates. I Renal Aspects. Arch Dis Child 1983; **58**: 335-342.

Bishop N. Bone disease in pre-term infants. Arch Dis Child 1989; **64**: 1403-1409.

Cartlidge P, Rutter N. Serum albumin concentrations and oedema in the newborn. Arch Dis Child 1986; **61**: 661-665.

Fletcher AB. The essential role of the laboratory in the optimal care of the sick neonate. JIFCC 1990; **2**: 166-172.

Haverden JM, Ward Platt MP. Metabolic adaptation in small for gestational age infants. Arch Dis Child 1993; **68**: 262-268.

Holland PC, Wilkinson AR, Diez J, Lindsell DRM. Prenatal deficiency of phosphate, phosphate supplemention and rickets in very low birthweight infants. Lancet 1990; **335**: 697-701.

Lucas A, Brooke OG, Baker BA, Bishop N, Morley R. High alkaline phosphatase activity and growth in pre-term neonates, Arch Dis Child 1989; **64**: 902-909.

Mayne PD, Kovar IZ. Calcium and phosphorus metabolism in the premature infant. Ann Clin Biochem 1991; **28**: 131-142.

Szymonowicz W, Yu VJH, Walker A, Wilson F. Reduction in periventricular haemorrhage in pre-term infants. Arch Dis Child 1986; **61**: 661-665.

Taghizadeh A, Reynolds EOR. Pathogenesis of bronchopulmonary dysplasia following hyaline membrane disease. Amer J Path 1979; **82**: 241-258.

Wilkins BH. Renal function in sick very low birth weight infants. Arch Dis Child 1992; **67**: 1140-1166.

Chapter 5

Neonatal Screening

INTRODUCTION

There are well established criteria for selecting disorders for neonatal screening (Table 5.1) Whole population screening programmes for phenylketonuria (PKU) and congenital hypothyroidism (CHT) exist throughout the United Kingdom. Babies are screened when they are between 6 and 14 days old by taking a small capillary sample of blood from a heel-prick stab. Programmes for PKU using blood commenced in the late 1960s and replaced the earlier methods using urine (Phenistix test) which had proved to be unreliable. Programmes for CHT were added in the early 1980s. In most parts of the U.K., screening is organised on a Regional basis with a centralised screening laboratory. This offers advantages of cost-effectiveness associated with large scale screening but, more importantly, concentrates information, facilitates audit and promotes development of expertise for these relatively rare disorders.

Table 5.1   Criteria for selection of disorders for neonatal screening

• Definition of the abnormality	—	Is the abnormality adequately defined?
• Population to be screened	—	What is considered to be the appropriate population to screen?
• Incidence	—	Have studies been carried out to establish incidence of the condition?
• Screening methods	—	Is a suitable, efficient and cost-effective method available?
• Follow-up procedures	—	Are diagnostic tests available and is there an acceptable treatment?
• Monitoring the effects	—	Is the natural history of the disease favourably effected by the screening procedure?
• Costs	—	What are the resource implications: education, operating costs, follow-up?
• Equivocal results	—	What is to be done about 'borderline' results?

Screening not only involves the specimen collection procedures and analytical procedures but also the communication and advisory service following the finding of a positive result. Another important part of such a service includes education of other health professionals (e.g., midwives, health visitors) involved in the service.

It is important that the quality and effectiveness of such a screening service be monitored. Data on the number of cases diagnosed, false positive and false negatives, age at diagnosis and start of treatment, age of babies tested and eventual outcome are all important measures. The practical aspects of screening are discussed in detail on pages 84-87.

PHENYLKETONURIA (PKU)

NEONATAL SCREENING AND MANAGEMENT IN CHILDHOOD

Phenylketonuria is an autosomal recessively inherited disorder due to deficiency of the enzyme phenylalanine hydroxylase (Fig 5.1). The gene resides on the long arm of chromosome 12 and molecular biology techniques have allowed the characterisation of more than 70 different mutations causing this enzyme deficiency. The extent of the enzyme deficiency varies from complete absence to a residual activity as high as 25%, depending on the particular mutation. A high proportion of affected individuals are compound heterozygotes, although a few specific mutations may account for the majority of cases in a particular population.

When phenylalanine hydroxylase is deficient, phenylalanine accumulates following commencement of normal milk feeding. By day six there is a high bloodconcentration of phenylalanine, usually in excess of 1000 µmol/L which, if untreated, would cause severe and irreversible mental handicap. The phenolicacid metabolites of phenylalanine, i.e., phenylpyruvate, phenyllactate and o-hydroxyphenylacetate also accumulate and are excreted in large quantities in the urine. The incidence of phenylketonuria varies widely but in most countries with screening programmes it lies between 1/5000 and 1/20000 live births. In the United Kingdom the average incidence is 1 in 10000 with a carrier frequency of 1 in 50.

The diagnosis is confirmed by the finding of a plasma phenylalanine concentration in excess of 1000µmol/L (normal <100µmol/L), with other amino acids notincreased, normal liver enzymes and normal biopterin investigations (see

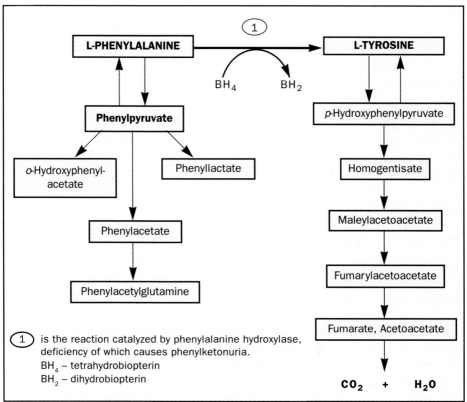

Fig 5.1   Metabolism of phenylalanine and tyrosine

below). For a baby detected on the neonatal screening programme with a gross increase in phenylalanine which is confirmed by quantitative analysis, a 'presumptive' diagnosis of 'classical' PKU is made and dietary treatment is commenced whilst awaiting the results of the biopterin investigations.

It is important that the diet should commence as soon as possible to ensure optimal outcome. The basis of the diet is a low phenylalanine content supplemented with a 'protein substitute' which is either a mixture of free L-amino acids or a protein hydrolysate free from phenylalanine. Products are available on prescription and those suitable for neonates include Analog XP, Minafen and Lofenalac. The protein substitutes now generally available have vitamins and minerals added to them, although Minafen requires additional supplements to prevent deficiencies occurring. A small and controlled amount of dietary phenylalanine intake is essential for normal growth and development. This is provided as 50mg 'exchanges' and in the neonate is provided as formula milk. Breast feeding can continue by giving the baby the protein substitute first and then 'topping up' with breast milk. Regular monitoring of plasma phenylalanine concentration is required, particularly during the first few weeks of treatment. Dietary phenylalanine is increased or decreased according to the plasma concentration. Blood-taking can be performed at home by parents and specimens, either as dried blood spots or liquid blood, sent to the laboratory by post. Current practice is to recommend that plasma phenylalanine be maintained between 120and 360 μmol/L during the first four years of life, with an upper limit of 480μmol/L after four years. Once the plasma concentration has stabilised, the frequency of monitoring can be reduced to weekly, and then to fortnightly intervals after the age of four years. More frequent monitoring is required if there is a particular problem with illness or compliance.

The strict dietary treatment is maintained until the child is ten years of age and then the option of a more 'relaxed' diet to maintain plasma phenylalanine concentrations below 800 μmol/L can be discussed. When approaching 17 years of age, discussion with the patient and family about the pros and cons of complete dietary withdrawal should take place. Professional opinion on the optimal plasma phenylalanine concentrations and the desirability of dietary relaxation has changed recently. There is an increasing tendency to maintain stricter control with more frequent monitoring and allow less relaxation. The dietary regime is not easy, and expert dietetic support is essential.

With early treatment and good dietary management, the outcome for the patient with phenylketonuria is good, with normal growth and development. Although most children probably come close to their full intellectual potential, recent evidence suggests that some children, even though treated early, suffer a mild degree of neurological impairment.

With the advance of molecular biology, carrier detection and prenatal diagnosis using mutation analysis are now theoretically possible for most families. However, for most couples already with a child with PKU this has rarely been undertaken because of the good outcome from dietary treatment.

MATERNAL PHENYLKETONURIA

Pregnancy in girls with untreated phenylketonuria is associated with a highincidence of severe fetal damage. Mental retardation will occur in a large percentage (90%) and there is a high risk of microcephaly, intra-uterine growth retardation and congenital heart disease. The risk of these congenital abnormalities can be greatly reduced by strictly controlling the plasma phenylalanine preconception and throughout pregnancy.

There is currently a female population of child bearing age who will not have been screened as neonates and mothers of babies with unexplained microcephaly and/or congenital heart disease should therefore be screened for PKU. Some Maternity Hospitals check maternal urine routinely at the booking appointment using Phenistix. Others may screen 'at risk' groups by plasma amino acid chromatography.

Phenylketonuria is a complex metabolic disorder and the patients and families need regular and on-going support for blood-taking, dietary management, genetic counselling and liaison with schools and community services. Care is best provided by a multidisciplinary team which includes a Clinical Nurse Specialist.

BIOPTERIN VARIANTS
Tetrahydrobiopterin is an essential coenzyme for phenylalanine hydroxylase (Fig. 5.2) and also tyrosine and tryptophan hydroxylases.

Inherited defects of dihydropteridine reductase (DHPR) or biopterin synthesis result in tetrahydrobiopterin deficiency and hence defective hydroxylation of phenylalanine, thus causing hyperphenylalaninaemia. In addition to defective hydroxylation of phenylalanine, there is also defective hydroxylation of tyrosine and tryptophan and hence failure to produce the neurotransmitters dopamine and serotonin. These biopterin defects can result in severe neurological disorders which are not effectively treated with a low phenylalanine diet but require supplementation with neurotransmitters. Although they are rare (1-3% of all cases of inherited hyperphenylalaninaemia) it is essential that every baby found to have hyperphenylalaninaemia is tested for these defects so that appropriate therapy can be initiated if necessary. The tests involve measurement of erythrocyte or whole blood dihydropteridine reductase activity and total plasma or whole blood biopterin.

OTHER CAUSES OF HYPERPHENYLALANINAEMIA
Liver dysfunction e.g.,in neonatal hepatitis, galactosaemia and biliary atresia may cause a significant elevation of several plasma amino acids including phenylalanine. In this situation increased phenylalanine is usually associated

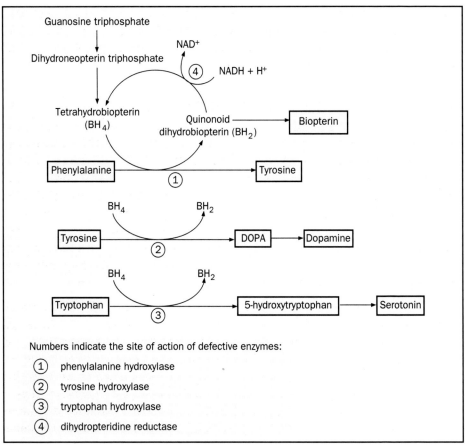

Fig 5.2   Biopterin metabolism

with abnormally high plasma tyrosine and possibly methionine concentrations. Some babies on total parenteral nutrition develop hyperphenylalaninaemia, although this is usually milder than in phenylketonuria with plasma phenylalanine concentrations well below 1000μmol/L (see p 132)

In addition to classical phenylketonuria, other genetic variants of the phenylalanine hydroxylase enzyme occur and are characterised by a persistent but mild increase of plasma phenylalanine (i.e., >100μmol/L), typically around 300-500μmol/L. It is thought that most of the affected individuals usually do not require dietary treatment as their plasma phenylalanine concentrations are within or close to the desirable treated range. They are usually clinically well and apart from an occasional (e.g., annual) check of their plasma phenylalanine, do not require more regular follow up. Females will require counselling as they approach child-bearing age.

CONGENITAL HYPOTHYROIDISM (CHT)

Congenital primary hypothyroidism is detected by neonatal screening programmesin about 1 in 3500 newborn infants (U.K. data). The majority of cases are caused by thyroid dysgenesis, with about 10% being due to dyshormonogenesis. Early replacement treatment with thyroxine can prevent brain damage and optimise outcome. Secondary pituitary hypothyroidism is very rare with an incidence of around 1 in 40000. Most screening programmes use thyroid stimulating hormone (TSH) rather than thyroxine as the former is the more sensitive measure. However, the few screening programmes which use thyroxine measurement as the primary screen may pick up the hypopituitary cases, which will not be detected by the programmes which use TSH.

Following a positive screening test, the diagnosis is confirmed by the finding of grossly elevated plasma TSH (in the majority of cases >200mU/L). Classical clinical features, e.g., lethargy, slow feeding, jaundice and constipation are absent in many cases. Following a positive screening test, the baby should be examined by a paediatrician as soon as possible. Treatment should not be delayed if there are any symptoms, however minimal, and L-thyroxine (10µg/kg/day) should be given once a blood specimen has been taken for definitive tests (i.e., TSH and free thyroxine). Thyroxine is administered orally by crushing the tablet with a little milk. If there are absolutely no clinical signs, it is usual to wait for confirmation of the repeat TSH test result before starting treatment. The repeat test for TSH should be arranged urgently and, if the diagnosis is confirmed, treatment should commence without further delay.

Not all cases of biochemical hypothyroidism detected by the neonatal screening programme are persistent and it is important in such cases to avoid unnecessary long-term treatment. For these reasons withdrawal of the treatment should be considered when the child is two years of age unless a thyroid scan reveals complete agenesis.

In order to keep the period without treatment to a minimum, triiodothyronine (T3) is substituted for thyroxine for 2-3 weeks before withdrawing the therapy

(T3 20μg/day ≡ T4 100μg/day). T3 is rapidly cleared from the circulation and therefore the plasma TSH and T4 measurements can be performed 2-4 days after stopping therapy.

For persistent CHT, treatment with thyroxine is continued throughout life with regular checks of plasma free thyroxine and TSH concentrations to ensure optimal replacement. The checks should be frequent during the first two years, and the results interpreted using appropriate reference ranges for age. Longitudinal prospective studies commenced in the 1980s have shown that although the outcome overall for treated CHT is good, school performance in some cases is below average. It is likely that those cases with severe hypothyroidism at birth have been compromised prenatally and are at greater risk of suffering long-term deficiency.

Some babies have mild but significant elevation of TSH with plasma concentrations up to 150 mU/L in the newborn period,which return to normal within a few weeks. In our experience this tends to occur particularly in Asian babies. Premature babies, particularly if they are 'sick' or have had surgery, often have higher TSH concentrations associated with low or low normal thyroxine concentrations. It may be beneficial to supplement such infants with thyroxine although conclusive data is not available.

PRACTICAL ASPECTS OF NEONATAL SCREENING

INTRODUCTION

In the United Kingdom screening tests are performed on a capillary blood specimen collected when the baby is between 6 and 14 days old. Most babies are at home at this age and the specimen is usually collected by the Community Midwife or more rarely by the Health Visitor. For those babies still in hospital, it is important that there is a system in place to ensure that these screening tests are not missed. This is particularly important for those babies still in Special Care Units because of 'prolonged jaundice' and those in specialist Intensive Care Units for whatever reason. There are several reports of late diagnosis of congenital hypothyroidism because a screening test was not done at six days whilst the baby was in hospital.

SCREENING TESTS

PKU is screened for by measuring phenylalanine in dried blood spots or liquid plasma. Three methods are in current use, these being the Guthrie microbiological assay, chromatography of amino acids, or an automated chemical method with fluorimetric detection. The Guthrie method is the most commonly used method and depends on excess phenylalanine to overcome the inhibition of growth of a particular strain of Bacillus subtilis by β-2-thienylalanine. The method can be used semi-quantitatively and will give an approximate phenylalanine concentration. The chromatographic method can be performed on paper (Scriver) or thin-layer plates and differs from the other two methods in that potentially certain other disorders of amino acid metabolism (e.g., maple syrup urine disease, tyrosinaemia) can be detected as well as PKU. Although this method offers possible advantages, in practice, for most populations, very few clinically significant disorders are detected in this way. The fluorimetric method is specific for phenylalanine. New enzymatic methods for measurement of plasma phenylalanine have recently become available although they have not yet been thoroughly evaluated for use as a screening procedure.

SPECIMEN REQUIREMENT

Blood specimens for neonatal screening are usually collected as spots on to thick absorbent cards which are allowed to dry before posting to the screening laboratory. Some screening laboratories use liquid blood collected into small plastic heparinised tubes. Glass capillary tubes should not be used because of health risks from high risk specimens.

It is important that babies have received sufficient milk feeds to allow reliable detection of PKU by routine screening procedures. This can be achieved by ensuring that the baby has been receiving normal milk feeds for 72 hours prior to the blood being taken. PKU can be successfully detected much earlier than six days and in certain situations where there is a high risk, i.e., sib of a known PKU patient, special arrangements can be made to test for phenylalanine much earlier, i.e., at three days of age. In such a situation it is important that the routine screening test for CHT and PKU (if the three day test is negative) is carried out at six days.

If a baby is not receiving milk feeds, the screening test should still be taken between 6-14 days to allow detection of CHT. A repeat test for PKU can then be arranged as soon as 72 hours of milk feeding have been achieved. The Guthrie method has the problem of possible false negative results for babies receiving antibiotics. It is usually apparent from the plate that there is inhibition of growth. In such a situation the test will usually be performed by another method (e.g., chromatography) or a repeat specimen collected. Antibiotic therapy does not interfere with the CHT screening procedure. Screening should never be delayed because of antibiotic therapy or any other reason.

In most screening programmes, CHT is detected by measurement of thyroid stimulating hormone (TSH) and in most centres the same blood spot card or liquid blood is used as for PKU screening. There are a few exceptions in the United Kingdom where thyroxine is the primary screening test. Although potentially T4 has the advantage of being a simpler and cheaper assay it has poor sensitivity and a large number of babies with CHT (30%) will have a T4 concentration within the normal neonatal range. For this reason T4 programmes require high cut-off points and a secondary TSH screen is performed on a fixed percentage of the batch. TSH is therefore the test of choice. However in most screening programmes, secondary hypothyroidism will be missed.

There are a variety of TSH methodologies in use, although the majority of screening laboratories still use well proven and robust radioimmunoassay technology. The trend away from isotopes (e.g., to fluoroimmunoassay), although desirable, may be difficult to justify because of the higher reagent costs associated with non-isotopic assays.

There is a surge of TSH during the first 24 hours of life (20-50mU/L whole blood) with return to normal concentrations (i.e., < 10mU/L) by day 5. Most screening methods have an upper limit of normal of 10mU/L for blood spot assays

FOLLOW-UP PROCEDURES

For both the PKU and CHT screening tests, rapid and effective follow-up procedures are required. The follow-up system will depend on the result of the test (Fig. 5.3) and may require immediate and direct referral to a paediatrician or involve a repeat test. Equivocal results may turn out to be negative on retest and it is important to minimise anxiety for parents. There are many causes for repeat specimens being requested (e.g., insufficient blood, specimen being lost in post, unsatisfactory analysis) and the reason for a repeat specimen being requested requires good communication with community services and, where appropriate, hospital paediatricians.

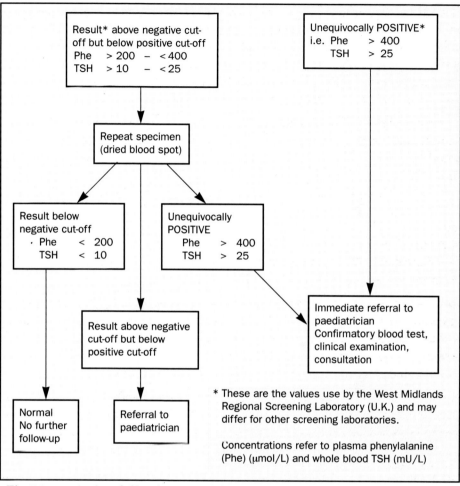

Fig 5.3   Action following a positive screening test

Referral mechanisms to ensure blood taking for confirmatory testing, clinical examination and, above all, communication of accurate and detailed information to anxious parents are essential. Close co-operation between the screening laboratory and other health care professionals involved is therefore important for successful follow-up. The finding of a positive case, whilst of great interest to health care professionals, is devastating news to the family of a newborn baby.

At the time of writing, neonatal screening programmes for CHT and PKU are well established in the developed countries. Other disorders which do not unequivocally fulfil all the criteria to justify whole population screening are screened for in some countries, either as established or pilot programmes e.g., congenital adrenal hyperplasia in some areas of the United States.

OTHER CONDITIONS

CYSTIC FIBROSIS (CF)

Cystic fibrosis is the commonest genetic disorder in Caucasians with an incidence of 1 in 2500 in many communities. Neonatal screening has been undertaken in several countries for many years by measurement of immunoreactive trypsin (IRT) in heel-prick blood. Experience with the IRT screening test has shown that it has poor specificity, which necessitates that a positive repeat test be obtained before pursuing definitive diagnosis by sweat testing and clinical examination. The case for screening has usually rested on the fact that most patients who have CF have a pre-symptomatic stage and that for many, diagnosis is often delayed with consequent anxiety to parents. An added point in favour of screening is that effective prenatal diagnosis is now available. Early diagnosis of CF in the baby or young infant will allow many parents the opportunity of prenatal diagnosis for the next pregnancy, whereas previously diagnosis of the propositus often came too late to prevent the birth of an affected sibling.

Although screening programmes using IRT lower the age at diagnosis and reduce the time spent in hospital in the first year of life, there are no data which unequivocally demonstrate that screening, followed by early initiation of a treatment protocol, significantly improves clinical outcome in the long-term.

An added problem with the screening programmes to date has been the less than ideal sensitivity and specificity of the IRT methodologies. A two tier approach using IRT followed by DNA analysis for the ΔF_{508} and other common mutations is being evaluated in some centres.

The possibility of large scale screening programmes to detect CF carriers with prenatal diagnosis for at-risk couples now exists; such a programme would negate the case for neonatal screening.

SICKLE CELL DISORDERS (SCD)

SCD i.e., homozygous HbSS, mixed heterozygous HbSC and mixed heterozygous HbS/β-thalassaemia, are common in the Afro-Caribbean population with a combined incidence of approximately 1 in 300 births. Infants with SCD are at risk of pneumococcal septicaemia and there is a high risk of death in the first year of life from sickle cell crises.

It has been found that early administration of prophylactic penicillin has a significant effect on reducing morbidity and mortality, and whole population screening programmes were established in various parts of the Unites States in the 1970s. In the United Kingdom programmes have been established in Birmingham and London, where the high percentage of Afro-Caribbeans justifies this approach. Provided that the baby has not been transfused, screening can be performed on the neonatal screening blood specimen by a combination of cellulose acetate and citrate agar electrophoresis of the haemoglobins. For the electrophoretic methods liquid blood specimens are preferable to dried blood spots as they produce a better quality of haemoglobin separation. The procedure requires experience in interpretation because of the large quantities of haemoglobin F present at six days of age. Alternative methods for dried blood spots e.g., isoelectric focusing, high pressure liquid chromatography, enzyme linked-immunoassasy, can be used. Currently, definitive confirmation of SCD cannot be made until the infant is 5-6 months of age, when the HbF has declined. However the diagnosis of carrier status in parents allows couples to be counselled about the risks for future pregnancies with an option for pre-natal diagnosis. Development of methodologies using DNA would allow immediate confirmation.

GALACTOSAEMIA (see p 113)

Galactosaemia is a relatively rare condition with an estimated incidence in the U.K. of approximately 1 in 45000 births. The justification for screening is based on prevention of neonatal mortality. Recent evidence however suggests that in spite of early treatment, long-term outcome is poor with neurological dysfunction and a high incidence of ovarian failure in females.

Screening is carried out in some parts of Europe and the United States and is usually performed by measurement of red cell galactose 1-phosphate by a microbiological method (Paigen method) or galactose 1-phosphate uridyl transferase (Gal 1-PUT) (Beutler method). Screening using the Beutler assay may produce a false negative result if the child has had a significant blood transfusion. Application of one of these assays to the blood screening samples that have slightly raised phenylalanine on the PKU screen may detect some cases of galactosaemia; increased phenylalanine (+/- tyrosine) is a feature of the liver dysfunction. Galactosaemia due to epimerase deficiency (see p 114) will not be detected by those methods which measure Gal 1-PUT.

Clinical awareness of the possibility of galactosaemia in the jaundiced and/or sick baby should enable prompt investigation and diagnosis without the need for a whole population screening programme. In the situtation where there is a newborn sibling of a known case of galactosaemia, the baby should be fed on a lactose-free formula (e.g., a soya-based formula such as Cow and Gate FormulaS) from birth until the result of the screening test becomes available.

CONGENITAL ADRENAL HYPERPLASIA (CAH) (see p 55)

Neonatal screening programmes by measurement of 17-hydroxyprogesterone in blood have been available in certain parts of the world since the early to mid 1980s. Incidence of 21-hydroxylase deficiency is variable but is estimated to be approximately 1 in 5000 to 1 in 15000 in Caucasian populations. Benefits are claimed to be avoidance of adrenal crises and reduced mortality and morbidity. The performance of some neonatal screening programmes is poor and false positive tests can occur; for example in some premature and low birth weight babies, ill babies and when blood specimens have been collected too early. Awareness of the possibility of CAH, particularly in newborns with sexual ambiguity, and babies with salt loss, has reduced the number of missed and late diagnoses in some populations without the need for whole population screening.

MISCELLANEOUS CONDITIONS

The disorders which can be screened for in the neonate are numerous with the commonest ones listed in Table 5.2 Mass screening programmes for glucose 6-phosphate dehydrogenase deficiency (see Ch 3) have been reported from Malaysia, Greece and parts of Italy. In parts of the United States, screening for biotinidase deficiency, maple syrup urine disease and homocystinuria takes place. Although the criteria (Table 5.1) for selection of disorders for neonatal screening have not changed, the ability to screen and availability of antenatal diagnosis for high risk families are now powerful influences to extend screening to other disorders.

Prospects for the future for neonatal screening are interesting and exciting. DNA analysis can already be performed on dried blood spots and will undoubtedly

Table 5.2   Disorders which can be detected by neonatal screening programmes

Disorder		Antenatal diagnosis an established option
Phenylketonuria	(1)	+
Congenital hypothyroidism	(1)	
Cystic fibrosis	(2)	+
Sickle cell disorders	(2)	+
Galactosaemia	(2)	+
Congenital adrenal hyperplasia		+
Duchenne muscular dystrophy	(2)	+
Biotinidase deficiency		
Homocystinuria	(2)	
Maple syrup disease		+
Glucose 6-phosphate dehydrogenase deficiency		
Beta-thalassaemia		+

(1)   National programme exists throughout United Kingdom and Ireland
(2)   Screening carried out in some parts of the United Kingdom and Ireland

have applications for detection of some inherited metabolic disorders in the future. The technology already exists to do this for several mutations causing cystic fibrosis and screening for medium chain acyl-CoA-dehydrogenase is an exciting possibility.

Familial hypercholesterolaemia is a potentially important area although the inability definitively to diagnose the disorder at a practical level, the enormous implications of counselling and reservations about the effectiveness of treatment, are reasons why the widespread development of mass newborn screening is not indicated at present. It is important however, that pilot programmes are established and evaluated.

Screening for some infectious diseases is possible and may be an important development area for the future. Anonymous testing for HIV as a prospective epidemiological study is established in parts of the U.K. using the dried blood spots collected for neonatal screening. Although not strictly for the neonate, pilot screening programmes for detecting neuroblastoma in infancy are currently under evaluation in many countries including the U.K.

FURTHER READING

Chatfield S, Owen G, Ryley HC, Williams J, Alfaham M, Goodchild MC et al. Neonatal screening for cystic fibrosis in Wales and the West Midlands: Clinical assessment after 5 years of screening. Arch Dis Child 1991; **66**: 29-33.

Guttler F. Phenylketonuria: 50 years since Follings' discovery and still expanding our clinical and biochemical knowledge. Acta Paed Scand 1984; **73**: 705-716.

Holton JB. Neonatal screening for biochemical disorders. Brit J Hosp Med 1988; **39**: 317-324.

John R. Screening for congenital hypothyroidism. Ann Clin Biochem 1987; **24**: 1-12.

Konecki DS, Lichter-Konecki U. The phenylketonuria locus; current knowledge about alleles and mutations of the phenylalanine hydroxylase gene in various populations. Hum Genet 1991; **87**: 377-388.

Medical Research Council Working Party on Phenylketonuria. Phenylketonuria due to phenylalanine hydroxylase deficiency: an unfolding story. Brit Med J 1993; **306**: 115-119.

Naylor EW. Recent developments in neonatal screening. Semin Perinatol 1985; **9**: 232-249.

Pang S, Dobbins RH, Kling S et al. Worldwide newborn screening update for classical congenital hyperplasia.

Schmidt BJ et al, editors. Current trends in infant screening: Proceedings of the 7th International Screening Symposium, Elsevier Science, 1989.

Report on the dietary management of phenylketonuria. Recommendations on the dietary management of phenylketonuria. Arch Dis Child 1993; **68**: 426-427.

Scriver CR, Kaufman S, Woo SLC. The hyperphenylalaninaemias; 15: 495-546. In:

Scriver CR et al, editors. The Metabolic Basis of Inherited disease, 6th edition. McGraw-Hill, New York, 1989.

Smith I. The hyperphenylalaninaemias. In:

Lloyd JK, Scriver CR, editors. Genetic and metabolic disases. Butterworths International Medical Reviews, Pediatrics 1985; 5: 166-209.

Smith I, Beasley MG, Ades A. Effect on intelligence of relaxing the low phenylalanine diet in phenylketonuria. Arch Dis Child 1990; 65: 311-316.

Smith I, Beasley MG, Ades A. Intelligence and quality of dietary treatment in phenylketonuria. Arch Dis Child 1990; 65: 472-478.

Smith I, Cook B, Measley M. Review of neonatal screening programme for phenylketonuria. BMJ 1991; 303: 333-335.

Whitby LG. Screening for disease: Definitions and criteria. Lancet 1974; II: 819-822.

Wilcken B, Webster D, editors. Neonatal screening into the '90s. Proceedings of the 8th International Screening Symposium, Leura, NSW, Australia and the Arthur Veale Memorial Meeting, Auckland, New Zealand. Kelvin Press, Australia 1991.

Chapter 6

Diagnosis of Inherited Metabolic Disorders (IMD)

INTRODUCTION

There are a large number of individually rare inherited disorders with a metabolic basis which present clinically in the neonatal period. Good data on the incidence of most IMD is not available, except where whole population screening programmes have been carried out. Incidence is extremely variable between different disorders and populations, ranging between 1 in 10000 and 1 in 200000. In spite of the rarity of individual disorders, collectively they present a sizeable problem.

The IMD which are most likely to present in the neonate are those due to defects in the metabolism of small molecules, i.e., amino acid, organic acid, carbohydrate and urea cycle defects. In addition, there are also some disorders of purine and pyrimidine metabolism and peroxisomal and lysosomal storage disorders which may present in the newborn. The disorders listed in Table 6.1 represent those which in the authors' experience are most likely to be encountered, although it is not an exhaustive list and there are other, rarer disorders which have been described.

Most babies with an IMD are born at or near term with normal birth weight and no abnormal features. Symptoms usually develop within the first week of life as full milk feeding is instituted. Exceptions to this include babies with an IMD born with associated dysmorphic features (see p 120). Also, some lysosomal storage disorders can present during pregnancy with fetal ascites and as a hydrops fetalis. A history of more than one pregnancy presenting in this way is suggestive of such a disorder and it is important to consider metabolic disease when no other cause of the hydrops has been found.

The biochemical basis of these disorders is wide ranging and there is a bewildering array of specialist tests. The best approach to investigation is to take careful note of any clues from the history, presentation and preliminary biochemical

Table 6.1   Inherited metabolic disorders which present in the neonate

• **Amino acid disorders**	Maple syrup urine disease
	Non-ketotic hyperglycinaemia
	Tyrosinaemia type I
	Homocystinuria (methylene tetrahydrofolate reductase variant)
• **Urea cycle disorders**	Carbamoyl phosphate synthetase deficiency
	Ornithine carbamoyl transferase deficiency
	Citrullinaemia
	Argininosuccinic acidaemia
• **Organic acid disorders**	Methylmalonic acidaemia
	Propionic acidaemia
	Isovaleric acidaemia
	Glutaric aciduria type II (multiple acyl-CoA dehydrogenase deficiency)
	Fatty acid oxidation defects
• **Carbohydrate disorders**	Galactosaemia
	Glycogen storage disease type I
	Fructose 1,6-diphosphatase deficiency
	Hereditary fructose intolerance
• **Congenital lactic acidoses**	Phosphoenolpyruvate carboxykinase deficiency
	Pyruvate carboxylase deficiency
	Electron transport chain defects
• **Peroxisomal disorders**	Zellweger's and Pseudo-Zellweger's syndromes
	Neonatal adrenoleucodystrophy
• **Purine and Pyrimidine disorders**	Sulphite oxidase and xanthine oxidase deficiency (molybdenum cofactor deficiency)
	Adenosine deaminase deficiency
• **Lysosomal storage disorders**	G_{M1} gangliosidosis
	Niemann Pick disease type C
	Krabbe's leucodystrophy
	Wolman's disease
	Pompe's disease
• **Others**	Menkes syndrome
	Congenital adrenal hyperplasia
	Sulphite oxidase deficiency (isolated)

tests and then proceed to the more specific investigations after discussion with a specialist laboratory.

PRESENTATION

CLUES FROM THE HISTORY

Consanguinity and family history of a similar illness in sibs or unexplained deaths are important. A history of male deaths particularly suggests an X-linked disorder such as ornithine carbamoyl transferase (OCT) deficiency.

It is particularly important to note if a previous sib has died following a 'Reye-like' illness as amino acid, urea cycle, organic acid and fatty acid oxidation defects can present in this way.

PRESENTATION/EXAMINATION

The 'classic' clinical presentation is the full-term baby born after a normal pregnancy and delivery who, after an initial symptom-free period, begins to deteriorate for no obvious reason. The time interval between birth and presentation may range from a few hours to weeks, depending on the nature of the defect, the feeding regime and the presence of other stress factors, particularly infection and surgery. The observation of a relationship between symptoms and a change in feeding regimes, e.g., changing to glucose/saline, a non-lactose milk formula, or reduced protein load, adds support to the possibility of an IMD and may suggest a particular diagnosis (e.g., galactosaemia, hereditary fructose intolerance).

In most cases the physical examination will not suggest a particular diagnosis as symptoms are non-specific, e.g., poor feeding, lethargy, vomiting, hypotonia, fits. Certain features are, however, particularly suggestive of IMD:

- abnormal smell, e.g., sweet, musty cabbage-like, sweaty (amino acid and organic acid disorders)
- cataracts (galactosaemia)
- hyperventilation, secondary to unexplained metabolic acidosis (organic acid disorders)
- unexplained hyponatraemia ± ambiguous genitalia (congenital adrenal hyperplasia)
- neurological dysfunction with respiratory alkalosis (urea cycle disorders)

It is important to be aware that diagnosis of an infection does not preclude an IMD and that sepsis is a common accompaniment to an underlying metabolic defect.

INVESTIGATION OF THE SICK NEONATE FOR IMD (See Protocol B)

PRELIMINARY 'ROUTINE' LABORATORY INVESTIGATIONS

Most sick neonates will have had a series of basic biochemical and haematological investigations carried out as part of their clinical care. If IMD is suspected, it can be particularly useful to review the results of these preliminary investigations before deciding to undertake the more specialized tests. Unexplained hypoglycaemia, hypocalcaemia, acid base disturbance and liver or neurological dysfunction are important clues and indicate the need for further investigations. Careful assessment of acid base status is required to unravel a compensated acidosis or a mixed metabolic and respiratory acidosis.

In a neonate with metabolic acidosis, calculation of the anion gap, i.e., $([Na^+] + [K^+]) - ([Cl^-] + [HCO_3^-])$, can be helpful, a gap >20mmol/L suggesting an organic acidaemia, whereas a normal gap is more likely to be due to renal tubular acidosis or bicarbonate loss from the gastrointestinal tract. A urine pH below 5.5 is suggestive of an organic acid disorder. A positive urine test for ketones is abnormal, although normal neonates may have a slightly positive result depending on the starvation state. A strongly positive result or a *negative result after prolonged fasting* is abnormal and indicates the need for detailed organic acid analysis.

A normal blood pH does not exclude an elevated plasma lactate and measurement of plasma lactate should always be considered if there is hypoglycaemia or neurological dysfunction, as well as in acidotic states. Unexplained anaemia may occur in some IMDs (e.g., pyroglutamic aciduria) and requires discussion with the specialist laboratory.

SPECIFIC METABOLIC INVESTIGATIONS

Certain abnormalities which may be revealed by the preliminary tests (i.e., hypoglycaemia, acidosis, liver dysfunction) suggest particular groups of metabolic disorders and should be investigated accordingly (see protocol B). Theresults of these preliminary investigations may sometimes suggest specific disorders and guide the order of priority for further tests. When there is any doubt as to how to proceed, dialogue with the specialist laboratory should ensure optimal investigation.

In the situation where the neonate is acutely ill then the following investigations should be considered and, when indicated, conducted urgently:

- ammonia (plasma)
- lactate (plasma)
- amino acids (urine and plasma)
- organic acids (urine)
- galactose 1-phosphate uridyl transferase (erythrocytes)

Where the baby is in a District General Hospital, these tests may not be available locally and arrangements to send specimens away for urgent investigation will be necessary. Ideally plasma ammonia and lactate should be available locally.

SPECIMEN COLLECTION FOR METABOLIC INVESTIGATIONS

If the baby has an episodic illness (e.g., related to diet) it is particularly important to collect blood and urine specimens during the acute phase as the diagnosis may be missed if specimens are collected only when 'well'. As a minimum, random urine (ideally 5mL but smaller quantities are valuable) and blood (at least 1mL heparin and 1mL fluoride oxalate) specimens should be collected, the plasma being separated and stored at -20°C. The packed red cells should be stored *unfrozen* at +4°C. If the child is severely ill and deteriorating, more rigorous specimen collection is indicated (see below and Protocol C).

With all specimens, an accurate recording of date and time of collection together with the following information should be provided :

(i) Feeding regime at the time of and immediately prior to sampling (this is particularly important if amino acids, organic acids and sugars are requested).

(ii) Details of all drug therapy or other treatment (including blood transfusions).

(iii) Full clinical details and results of any preliminary biochemical/haematological investigations and degree of urgency.

Details of drug therapy are particularly important for amino acid investigations as several antibiotics produce 'ninhydrin positive' spots.

LIFE THREATENING ILLNESS

If the illness is progressing rapidly and death seems inevitable, it is important to ensure that appropriate specimens (blood, urine, skin and tissues are taken for biochemical analysis to enable reliable post-mortem diagnosis (see Protocol C). Blood and urine should be taken *pre-mortem* whenever possible. Blood taken around the time of death or post-mortem will be of limited use as lactic acidosis, hyperammonaemia and hyperaminoacidaemia due to protein autolysis are likely to confuse the picture and make interpretation of the results at best difficult and often impossible. A detailed autopsy is most important and should be carried out as soon as possible after death to minimise specimen deterioration. For those families where a diagnosis can be made, genetic counselling and the opportunity for prenatal diagnosis for future pregnancies is of paramount importance and hence great efforts should be made to obtain these important specimens.

SUDDEN INFANT DEATH AND METABOLIC DISEASE

A small percentage of cases of sudden infant death syndrome (SIDS) have been associated with a metabolic defect of fatty acid oxidation. The most frequently reported defects in SIDS or in 'near miss' cot deaths are those of the medium chain acyl CoA dehydrogenase (MCAD) enzyme system (see p 111) although more rarely other metabolic defects have been described. It is therefore important to consider the possibility of metabolic disorders in infants dying suddenly, particularly those who are found to have a pronounced fatty change in the liver at autopsy. Even if there are no samples for biochemical investigation from the index case, in families where there is a high degree of suspicion, further children can be investigated immediately after birth for disorders of fatty acid oxidation. Urinary organic acids collected during the first two days of life may show the characteristic metabolites of MCAD deficiency although a negative result does not exclude this disorder. DNA can be tested for the common mutation associated with MCAD deficiency.

MANAGEMENT OF THE ACUTE SITUATION

(i)   Whilst awaiting results of specific investigations, management is supportive and geared to correcting electrolyte and acid base balance and maintaining adequate gas exchange. Regimes should be instituted to try to induce an anabolic state as quickly as possible. Replacement of milk feeds with dextrose infusion (oral or i.v.) is appropriate for most disorders i.e., amino acid, organic acid, urea cycle disorders and galactosaemia. However, this is not appropriate for the congenital lactic acidoses which are likely to be exacerbated by a high carbohydrate load.

(ii)   Severe hyperammonaemia, due to urea cycle defects, should be treated with sodium benzoate (see p 107).

(iii)   Several IMD have vitamin responsive variants and the approach in some units is to give a vitamin cocktail whilst awaiting results. If this approach is used, it is crucial that the appropriate specimens (blood and urine) have been taken before the vitamins are given. In practice, it is rare for an IMD presenting acutely in the neonate to be one of these vitamin responsive types.

(iv)   If more rigorous treatment is considered, e.g., exchange transfusion or dialysis, then this will usually require that the baby be transferred to a specialised clinical centre.

ANTENATAL DIAGNOSIS

Increasing numbers of metabolic disorders can be screened for in high risk families by obtaining fetal tissue. Usually the risk of an affected fetus for each pregnancy will be 1 in 4 as most conditions are inherited as autosomal recessive traits. Tissue can be obtained by chorionic villus biopsy either transcervically or transabdominally at about 10 weeks gestation. This procedure has about a 2% risk of leading to pregnancy failure (i.e., about double the risk of amniocentesis). For some of the rarer IMDs, chorionic villus biopsy is not yet a technique of proven value and amniocentesis is still the procedure of choice. In these latter situations diagnosis either requires enzyme measurement in the cultured amniocytes or metabolite measurement in the supernatant. Occasionally, much more high risk investigations may be undertaken such as fetal liver biopsy in the second trimester, e.g., for ornithine carbamoyl transferase deficiency (see p 107).

The general aim following such investigations would be to terminate the pregnancy if the fetus was found to be affected. Extensive counselling of the family, ideally before pregnancy, is therefore a mandatory part of such 'high risk' investigations.

'Routine' ultrasound is offered for all continuing pregnancies. Detailed scanning for structural abnormalities will be performed at 20-21 weeks of gestation.

Other structural abnormalities with biochemical consequences are increasingly being detected at these procedures. These include detection of significant renal abnormalities which can then be investigated and treated from birth, rather than waiting for them to present clinically.

DISORDERS PRESENTING AS A SICK NEONATE

AMINO ACID DISORDERS

Those defects, which cause accumulation of specific amino acids in blood, urine or CSF can be diagnosed by amino acid analysis. Quantitative plasma amino acid analysis is usually essential.

Maple Syrup Urine Disease (MSUD)

Characteristic presentation is with feeding difficulties, lethargy and failure to thrive with progressive CNS dysfunction. Biochemical abnormalities include metabolic acidosis and hypoglycaemia. In the classical form, urine and sweat have a characteristic sweet odour and the disorder is severe with a progressive downhill course which, if untreated, leads to early death. Milder variants have been described but these usually present later in infancy or early childhood with mild developmental delay. MSUD is due to a defective decarboxylation of the branched chain oxo acids (Fig. 6.1) If this disorder is particularly suspected, a positive dinitrophenylhydrazine screening test for oxo acids in urine provides a useful supporting clue. The definitive diagnosis is made by the finding of grossly increased concentrations of branched chain amino acids (leucine, isoleucine, and valine), in plasma together with the presence of alloisoleucine and an increase in the corresponding oxo acids in urine. Plasma amino acids may also show a reduced alanine. Treatment is to give a special diet low in the branched chain amino acids. Although the initiation of correct dietary therapy may be lifesaving, the longer term outlook is not ideal. There is a tendency for episodic bouts of illness with vomiting to occur, usually precipitated by an infection, and

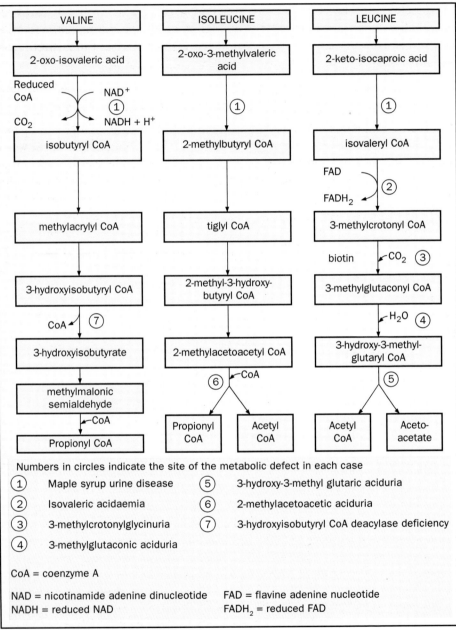

Fig 6.1   **Disorders of branched amino acid catabolism**

for impaired development. In the severe form, recognition of the diagnosis is potentially life saving and good dietary management can minimise the number and severity of episodic illnesses considerably. However, the long term prognosis for the classical form of the disorder is poor. Milder forms of the disease exist.

NON-KETOTIC HYPERGLYCINAEMIA (NKH)
Preliminary biochemical tests are usually normal and indication for investigation is based on the characteric clinical picture of a neonate with severe uncontrollable seizures, respiratory failure and hypotonia. The EEG (Fig. 6.2) shows a typical burst-suppression pattern and the baby is often noted to have hiccups. The basic defect lies inthe glycine cleavage system and diagnosis is based on the finding of an elevated plasma and CSF glycine with an abnormally high CSF:plasma glycine ratio. Rapid quantitative amino acid results are required in this situation so that other disorders, perhaps treatable, can be eliminated. There

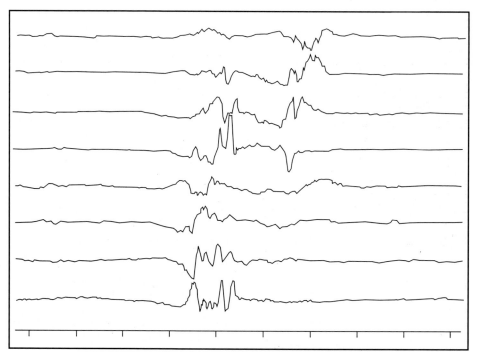

Fig 6.2   Electroencephalogram from a patient with non-ketotic hyperglycinaemia, showing characteristic burst-suppression pattern.

is no effective treatment for NKH and at the time of writing the possibilities for prenatal diagnosis are only experimental. Hyperglycinaemia associated with ketonuria is strongly suggestive of an organic acid disorder (e.g., methylmalonic acidaemia) and investigation of urinary organic acids is therefore essential in this situation.

TYROSINAEMIA TYPE I

The acute form of tyrosinaemia type I presents with severe liver disease and renal tubular dysfunction. The disease is due to a defect of the enzyme fumarylacetoacetase (Fig. 6.3) which causes accumulation of succinylacetoneand secondary increases of tyrosine, *p*-hydroxyphenylpyruvate and *p*-hydroxyphenyl lactate due to inhibition of *p*-hydroxyphenylpyruvate oxidase.

In the neonate, the presenting feature may be hypoglycaemia progressing to fulminant liver failure. Diagnosis is suspected by the finding of increased plasma

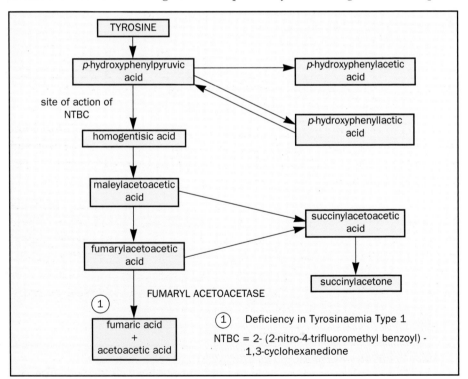

Fig 6.3   Catabolism of tyrosine

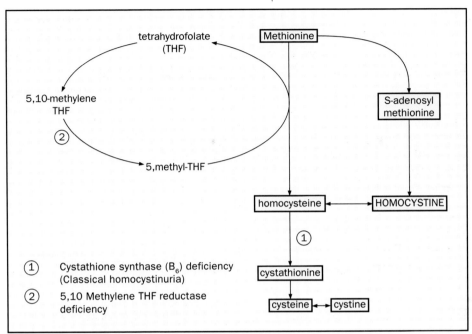

Fig 6.4   **Metabolism of homocystine showing the defective enzymes in homocystinuria**

tyrosine concentrations, often associated with increased methionine and phenylalanine. A useful biochemical clue to support the diagnosis is a very high plasma alkaline phosphatase activity (>2000IU/L). The important test to perform in this situation is measurement of urinary succinyl acetone.

Definitive diagnosis requires measurement of fumarylacetoacetase in cultured skin fibroblasts or leucocytes. Immediate treatment is dietary with the possibility of liver transplantation at a later stage. Without transplantation a large percentage of cases will develop hepatoma. Recently a new compound, NTBC (see Fig 6.3) which inhibits *p*-hydroxyphenylpyruvate oxygenase has been used in a few patients and may offer an alternative to liver transplantation. Prenatal diagnosis is possible by chorionic villus biopsy or amniocentesis.

HOMOCYSTINURIA
(DUE TO 5,10-METHYLENE TETRAHYDROFOLATE REDUCTASE DEFICIENCY)
Classical homocystinuria due to cystathionine synthase deficiency does not present in the neonate although some neonatal screening programmes may

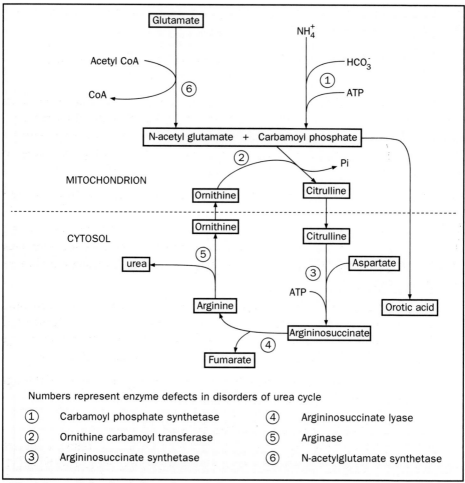

Numbers represent enzyme defects in disorders of urea cycle

①   Carbamoyl phosphate synthetase   ④   Argininosuccinate lyase

②   Ornithine carbamoyl transferase   ⑤   Arginase

③   Argininosuccinate synthetase   ⑥   N-acetylglutamate synthetase

Fig 6.5   **Inherited disorders of the urea cycle**

detect the disorder. The variant form, due to defective remethylation, (see Fig 6.4) can however present in the neonatal period with apnoeic episodes, fits, and progressive CNS dysfunction.

Diagnosis requires a careful search for homocystine in blood and urine. This requires *fresh* specimens. Plasma must be deproteinised promptly. The finding of a low or low-normal plasma methionine concentration and the presence of homocystine in urine and plasma is consistent with this defect. The diagnosis can be confirmed by demonstrating the enzyme defect in cultured skin fibroblasts. Treatment with betaine should be considered.

UREA CYCLE DISORDERS (UCD) AND HYPERAMMONAEMIA

Urea Cycle Disorders
There are six inherited disorders of the urea cycle (Fig 6.5) which can present in the neonate with hyperammonaemia. Plasma ammonia concentrations in excess of 800µmol/L in the first 1-3 days of life life are characteristic of the severe forms of UCD although the ammonia level is dependent on protein intake and may be much lower than this if milk feeding has been reduced or withdrawn.

Onset is usually very early (i.e., within 48h of birth) and initial features include lethargy, feed refusal, vomiting, irritability, seizures and tachypnoea. Ammonia is a respiratory stimulant and the presence of a respiratory alkalosis is an important diagnostic clue. A family history of male neonatal deaths suggests OCT deficiency. Liver failure may develop and pulmonary or intracranial haemorrhage can occur.

In addition to the UCDs some organic acid disorders, in particular methylmalonic and propionic acidaemia, can present in the neonate with significant hyperammonaemia (400-800µmol/L). Hyperammonaemia with acidosis and ketonuria is particularly suggestive of an underlying organic acid disorder.

The importance of investigating urinary organic acids as part of the differential diagnosis of neonatal hyperammonaemia cannot be over emphasised.

Further Investigation of Neonatal Hyperammonaemia
Hyperammonaemia is not a diagnosis on its own and further investigations are required urgently to establish the cause. Additional biochemical tests which should be performed are :

- tests for liver dysfunction: alanine aminotransferase, alkaline phosphatase, bilirubin (total & conjugated or direct), albumin, prothrombin time.

- plasma amino acids

- urine amino acids

- urine organic acids

- urine orotic acid

TREATMENT

Hyperammonaemia (greater than 200μmol/L) requires prompt treatment to minimise the risks of permanent neurological handicap.

Whilst awaiting the results of further investigations dietary protein should be withdrawn or reduced whilst ensuring the provision of adequate calories from other substrates. If the situation deteriorates, with worsening of the clinical state and/or rising ammonia concentrations or grossly elevated concentrations which fail to fall significantly, aggressive therapy should be considered. Treatment with sodium benzoate and/or sodium phenylbutyrate can be used to promote excretion of nitrogen containing compounds (see below). In severe cases, dialysis may be indicated. Haemodialysis is preferable to peritoneal dialysis if expertise is available. Exchange transfusion is of little value in this situation as the benefits are transient. Patients with the severest types of UCD, even with early treatment, have a poor outcome and discussion about the desirability of continuing long-term treatment is required.

The basis of long-term treatment of the UCD is dietary protein restriction (0.8-1.5g/kg/24h). Sodium benzoate and/or sodium phenylbutyrate therapy may also be necessary to keep plasma ammonia concentrations down to an acceptable level (<80μmol/L). Benzoate conjugates with glycine to form hippurate which is excreted and thereby diverts nitrogen away from the urea cycle. Sodium phenylbutyrate (or sodium phenylacetate) is converted to phenylacetylglutamine and excreted, thereby removing two nitrogen atoms. In severe cases benzoate and phenylbutyrate can be given in combination. Benzoic acid may be hepatotoxic and theoretically will displace bilirubin from albumin; it therefore may be a particular risk in the jaundiced neonate. With the exception of argininaemia, arginine becomes an essential amino acid in patients with a UCD and supplements are therefore required.

Treatment regimes require regular monitoring of plasma ammonia and relevant amino acids. Measurment of plasma benzoate is desirable to ensure that toxic concentrations are not produced.

OTHER CAUSES OF HYPERAMMONAEMIA IN THE NEONATE

In addition to the inherited disorders, there is a condition termed 'transient hyperammonaemia of the newborn' which can present as an overwhelming life-threatening illness in the first 48h of life. The condition is more likely to occur in the pre-term baby (<36 weeks gestation) and usually presents with respiratory distress within 24h of birth. Plasma ammonia concentration is very high, usually in excess of 1500μmol/L, and urinary orotic acid concentration is normal. Outcome is good if the condition is treated promptly and aggressively. Presentation may be indistinguishable from those IMD presenting with hyperammonaemia and a presumptive diagnosis is made by exclusion, after careful assessment of plasma and urinary amino acids, urinary organic acids and orotic acid.

Although hyperammonaemia as a complication of total parenteral nutrition is rare, it should be considered if the baby is lethargic or showing signs of CNS dysfunction. It is more likely to occur in low birth weight babies.

It is important to note that sick pre-term neonates, in the absence of an inherited metabolic disease, may have moderate elevation of plasma ammonia (up to 200μmol/L) particularly if there is infection or asphyxia.

ORGANIC ACID DISORDERS
DEFECTS OF BRANCHED CHAIN AMINO ACID AND PROPIONYL COA CATABOLISM
Organic acids are carboxylic acids of low molecular weight and are metabolites of amino acids, carbohydrates and fats. Several intermediary metabolic pathways are affected, the major ones being the catabolism of the branched chain amino acids, leucine, isoleucine and valine (Fig 6.1) and propionyl CoA (Fig 6.6). The intermediates which accumulate in these disorders do not react with ninhydrin and therefore cannot be diagnosed by amino acid analysis. Specific methods for organic acids using gas chromatography-mass spectrometry are therefore essential. Over 50 disorders due to a primary biochemical defect of organic acid metabolism have been described and their combined incidence is probably at least as great as that of amino acid disorders.

Presentation in the neonatal period is usually as a severe metabolic acidosis with lethargy, vomiting and hypotonia. There are often other metabolic abnormalities associated with the acidosis, for example:

- hypoglycaemia
- hyperammonaemia
- hypocalcaemia
- ketonuria
- hyperlactataemia
- hyperuricaemia
- neutropenia
- increased plasma and urine glycine.

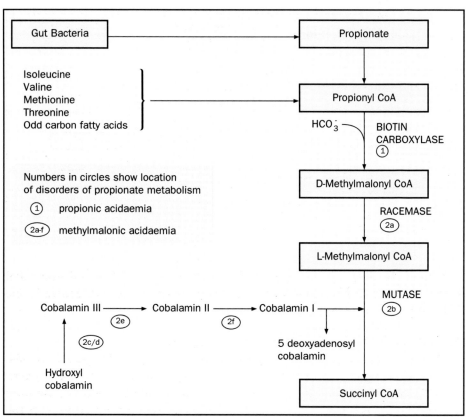

Fig 6.6 **Formation and metabolism of propionyl coenzyme A (CoA)**

Whilst awaiting results of investigations, dietary protein should be withdrawn. Diagnosis of these disorders requires detailed investigation of urine by gas chromatography–mass spectrometry.

A *fresh* random urine is required, preferably collected whilst the baby is acidotic and before dietary protein is withdrawn. Treatment is by dietary protein restriction (0.8-1.5g/kg/day) sometimes in combination with an artificial amino acid mixture. Some units recommend treatment with a vitamin cocktail. However, the basis for this is unproven as although there are vitamin responsive forms of these disorders these are less likely to be the types which present acutely in the neonate.

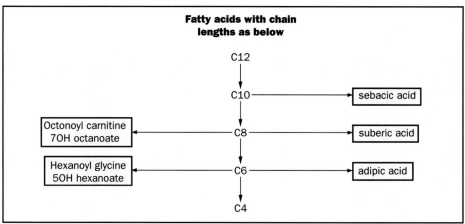

Fig 6.7 **Fatty acid oxidation**

Unfortunately, despite treatment, patients who have presented in the neonatal period continue to have intermittent crises of ketoacidosis and generally the long-term outcome is poor.

DISORDERS OF FATTY ACID OXIDATION.
This particular group of disorders characteristically present with hypoglycaemia. *Any neonate or infant with unexplained hypoglycaemia should have a urine specimen collected for organic acid investigations at the time of presentation.* These disorders are due to defects in the β-oxidation of fatty acids and consequent impairment of the conversion of fatty acids to ketone bodies. The hypoglycaemia is therefore characteristically associated with an inappropriately low concentration of plasmaand urine ketones and an abnormally high ratio of plasma free fatty acids: 3-hydroxybutyrate. During conditions of stress, e.g., fasting, catabolism, the fatty acid esters and corresponding dicarboxylic acids e.g., sebacic, suberic and adipic acids accumulate (see Fig 6.7).

Several defects have been described, differing on the basis of the fatty acid chain length which is affected. The commonest disorder described is the defect of the medium chain acyl CoA dehydrogenase (MCAD) system affecting fatty acids of carbon length C6 to C10.

Diagnosis of these conditions can be very difficult, as urinary organic acids may be completely normal when the infant is well and abnormalities may only

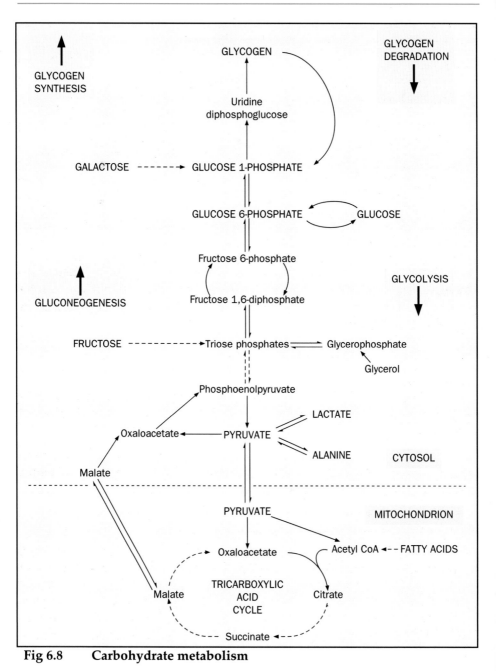

Fig 6.8   Carbohydrate metabolism

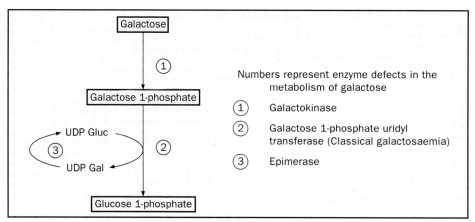

Fig 6.9   **Disorders of galactose metabolism**

become evident when he is stressed by starvation. It is particularly important to investigate newborn sibs of known cases by looking for characteristic metabolites in urine which has been collected within the first 72h of life when the baby is stressed from the birth process.

CARBOHYDRATE DISORDERS (FIG 6.8)

GALACTOSAEMIA

Classical galactosaemia, due to galactose 1-phosphate uridyl transferase deficiency (Fig 6.9), characteristically presents with failure to thrive, jaundice and hepatomegaly. The incidence in the U.K. is approximately 1:45000.

The severe illness is frequently associated with septicaemia and without treatment death may ensue. In most of the United Kingdom there is no whole population screening (see p 89) and initial diagnosis relies on clinical acumen.

Diagnosis is supported by the finding of positive urinary reducing substances (Clinitest) but the definitive test is measurement of galactose 1-phosphate uridyl transferase (Gal 1-PUT) in erythrocytes. A negative test for urinary reducing substances *provided the baby is on lactose containing milk formula,* is a simple and effective way of excluding classical galactosaemia. If the baby is on a non-lactose formula, if the milk intake has been reduced, or the baby has severe vomiting this test is *not* a reliable way of excluding the diagnosis and the Gal 1-PUT test *must* be performed. 'Screening' type assays for Gal 1-PUT (e.g., Beutler test) are usually available in specialist laboratories and enable results to be provided within half a working day. If the diagnosis is suspected the baby should be taken off lactose whilst awaiting the results of the screening test. This is particularly important for the newborn sib of a confirmed case. An abnormal screening test should always be confirmed with a quantitative assay as the heterozygous state cannot always be reliably differentiated and also several enzyme variants (e.g., Duarte allele) exist. Epimerase deficiency (Fig. 6.9) has been described in a few cases and can present with a similar clinical picture to transferase deficiency; this deficiency should be considered if there is persistent galactosuria and a normal Gal 1-PUT.

False positive Beutler screening tests can occur if the red cells are deficient in glucose 6-phosphate dehydrogenase. A high haemoglobin concentration can interfere with the test, making interpretation of the results difficult and possibly giving rise to a false positive screening test. A false negative result will occur if the baby has recently had a blood transfusion and therefore the test is not valid if carried out within six weeks of a major transfusion. Persistent galactosuria in a baby must be taken seriously and a diagnosis pursued vigorously — the neonatologist and clinical biochemist should be aware of the possibility of a false negative result. If the baby has a 'classical' galactosaemia picture with galactosuria, tyrosinaemia type I (p 104) and hereditary fructose intolerance (p 115) should be considered as part of the differential diagnosis.

Untreated galactosaemic babies are susceptible to *E.coli* sepsis and this disorder should be considered when jaundice, hepatomegaly and sepsis occur in a neonate.

The treatment of galactosaemia is life long treatment with a galactose-free diet. Recovery from the acute life-threatening stage is usually rapid and complete. Dietary compliance should be monitored by measurement of erythrocyte galactose 1-phosphate. The long-term outcome for patients with treated galactosaemia is unclear. Recent evidence suggests that in a significant number of patients, although treated from an early age, there is some degree of neurological handicap in the long-term.

GLYCOGEN STORAGE DISEASE (GSD) TYPE I
This is a group of disorders due to a deficiency of glucose 6-phosphatase; patients with the disease can present within the first few days of life with hypoglycaemia and metabolic acidosis. The liver may be enlarged and activity of plasma liver enzymes increased. Neutropenia is a feature of some types . Biochemical features include hypoglycaemia, and increased plasma lactate, triglycerides, cholesterol, and urate concentrations. Liver biopsy shows excess

glycogen and associated fatty change. Diagnosis of the classical form requires measurement of glucose 6-phosphatase activity in liver tissues as the enzyme is not expressed in cultured skin fibroblasts or red blood cells. Patients with a clinical, biochemical and histological picture of glycogen storage disease type I but with normal activity of glucose 6-phosphatase in frozen liver tissue should be further investigated for the variant types of GSD I. The variant form type Ib can be diagnosed by performing the enzyme assay on *fresh* (not frozen) liver tissue. Tolerance tests (e.g., glucagon, galactose, glucose) are not appropriate in the young baby/infant and it is far better to proceed directly to histological investigation and specific enzyme measurements.

In some cases, the presentation is not so fulminant and cases have been described where a baby has had unexplained hypoglycaemic episodes soon after birth, from which there was apparent full recovery until the infant presented several months later with unexplained hepatomegaly. Such cases stress the importance of adequately investigating hypoglycaemia (see p 45).

The main feature of this disorder is repeated hypoglycaemic episodes with elevated blood lactate. Treatment is geared to prevent or minimise hypoglycaemia and some patients manage with frequent feeds of a carbohydrate-rich diet For others continuous tube feeding is required. The use of corn starch as a carbohydrate source has improved management and as the child gets older, the frequency of attacks usually reduces. Long-term complications of renal and liver function can occur and follow up with relevant biochemical and clinical monitoring is required.

DISORDERS OF FRUCTOSE METABOLISM

Hereditary Fructose Intolerance (HFI).
This disorder only presents after exposure to fructose (or sucrose) and is therefore very rare in neonates. Presentation is very similar to galactosaemia and removal of the dietary sugar results in rapid clinical and biochemical improvement. Biochemical features include hypophosphataemia, hypoglycaemia and increased plasma lactate concentration. The diagnosis may be suspected from detailed nutritional history, clinical picture, the finding of a positive test for urinary reducing substances and aminoaciduria.

Measurement of the enzyme fructose 1,6-diphosphate aldolase activity in liver tissue is required for definitive diagnosis. Fructose tolerance tests, either oral or i.v., are not recommended in neonates or young infants.

Fructose 1,6-Diphosphatase Deficiency
In contrast to HFI, dietary ingestion of fructose is not a prerequisite to presentation. Acute presentation in the neonate is similar to glycogen storage disease type I, comprising hypoglycaemia, metabolic (lactic) acidosis, convulsions and hepatomegaly. Definitive diagnosis requires measurement of fructose 1,6-diphosphatase activity in liver tissue.

LACTIC ACIDOSIS
The commonest cause of severe lactic acidosis is hypoxia/ischaemia (see p 139). When considering metabolic causes of lactic acidosis, it is therefore important to ensure that the baby is well perfused and has adequate intravascular blood volume and blood pressure. Poor peripheral circulation will occur following intraventricular haemorrhage and in the hypoplastic left heart syndrome. Levels of plasma lactate greater than 10mmol/L can occur during hypoxia and excessive muscular activity.

A moderately increased blood lactate concentration (2-4mmol/L) may occur in infection, dehydration states, or if there is liver dysfunction. Fitting can cause a significant increase in lactate in any infant, presumably as a result of relative hypoxia and excessive muscular activity.

If these causes have been excluded, a persistent and significantly elevated lactate (i.e., >3mmol/L) requires further investigation for the possibility of an IMD. This is particularly likely if associated with hypoglycaemia. Differential diagnoses include:

- glycogen storage disorder type I

- organic acid disorders including fatty acid oxidation defects

- disorders of pyruvate metabolism (pyruvate dehydrogenase deficiency)

- disorders of gluconeogenesis (phosphoenolpyruvate carboxykinase, pyruvate carboxylase, fructose 1,6-diphosphatase deficiencies)

- electron transport chain defects.

Further tests which should be undertaken include measurement of urinary organic acids, plasma urate, plasma creatine kinase, plasma and urine amino acids, fasting glucose, and liver enzyme tests. Results of these tests may be useful in establishing the significance of a mild or intermittent lactic acidosis and in guiding further investigations.

Urinary organic acids may not show an increased lactate if the plasma lactate does not exceed 7mmol/L. Normal urinary organic acids therefore do not preclude the possibility of a significantly increased plasma lactate.

If investigations for glycogen storage disorders, organic acid disorders and fructose 1,6-diphosphatase deficiency are negative, then investigations for inborn errors of pyruvate metabolism and the electron transport chain require discussion with specialists in the field. Very complex tests (usually requiring tissue samples) are required to make these particular diagnoses. The final results of such investigations may not be available for many months and in many cases a definitive diagnosis will not be made.

PEROXISOMAL DISORDERS
The peroxisome is a subcellular organelle containing many enzyme systems. Functions include biosynthesis of plasmalogens (essental neuronal lipid compounds), catalase activity, oxidation of very long, long and medium chain fatty

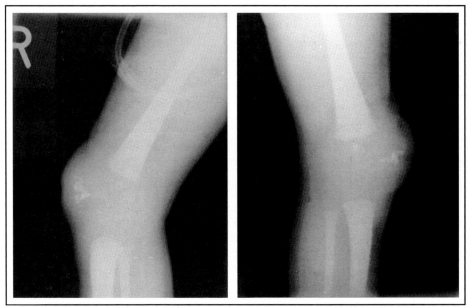

Fig 6.10   Radiograph showing calcific stippling of the epiphyses in a three week old patient with Zellweger's Syndrome

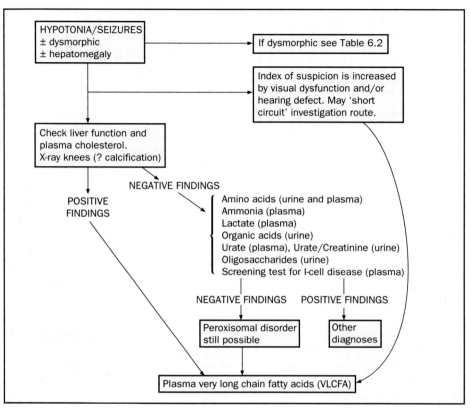

Fig 6.11   Investigation of neonate with hypotonia and seizures

acids and metabolism of pipecolic acid (a metabolite of lysine oxidation). A range of inherited metabolic disorders have been described due to single or multiple defects in peroxisomal function.

The classic disorder of this group is Zellweger's syndrome. The major clinical features are dysmorphism, hypotonia, liver dysfunction, hepatomegaly and developmental delay. Presentation is at birth or shortly afterwards, often with seizures and severe hypotonia. The radiographic finding of calcific stippling of the epiphyses demonstrable on X-ray (Fig. 6.10) is an important clue. There are no simple biochemical tests; diagnosis requires measurement of plasma very long chain fatty acids (VLCFA).

Other investigations should be considered in a baby with hypotonia and seizures (see protocol, Fig 6.11).

Table 6.2   Some metabolic disorders which may present with dysmorphic features in the neonate

	Dysmorphic features	Other features	Specific investigation(s)
Maternal PKU	Microcephaly	Congenital heart disease	Plasma phenylalanine in mother
Congenital lactic acidosis (pyruvate dehydrogenase deficiency)	Abnormal facies Microcephaly	Acidosis Hypotonia Seizures Abnormal brain (absence of corpus callosum)	Blood (& CSF) lactate Fibroblast studies Pyruvate oxidation DNA analysis
Zellweger's Syndrome and related disorders	High forehead Shallow supra-orbital ridges Epicanthic folds Abnormal ear helices High arched palate Micrognathia Large fontanelle	Hypotonia Hepatomegaly Seizures Calcific stippling of epiphyses	Red cell membrane Plasmalogens Platelet and fibroblast dihydroxyacetone phosphate acyl transferase Plasma C26/C24 fatty acid ratios
Glutaric aciduria Type II (multiple acyl CoA dehydrogenase deficiency)	Macrocephaly Abnormal facies	Hypotonia Hypoglycaemia Polycystic kidneys	Urinary organic acids Lymphocyte/fibroblast fatty acid oxidation
Sulphite/xanthine oxidase deficiency (Molybdenum cofactor deficiency)	Abnormal facies	Seizures Hypotonia	Urine sulphite Plasma urate Urine urate/creatinine
Congenital adrenal hyperplasia	Ambiguous genitalia in females	Salt loss Recurrent vomiting Dehydration Hyponatraemia	Plasma 17-hydroxy-progesterone
Congenital hypothyroidism	Coarse facies	Jaundice Constipation	Serum thyroid stimulating hormone and free thyroxine
G_{M1} Gangliosidosis	Frontal bossing Depressed nasal bridge Low set ears	Feeding difficulties Hypoactive Hypotonia Oedema	Urinary GAGs White cell/fibroblast βgalactosidase
Mucolipidosis 2 (ICell disease)	Course facies Depressed nasal bridge Large tongue	Restricted joint movement Radiological changes	Plasma arylsulphatase A (I-Cell screen)
Mucolipidosis 1 (Sialidosis)	Course facies Depressed nasal bridge Large tongue	Radiological changes Cherry red spot myoclonus	White cell/fibroblast neuraminidase Urinary oligosaccharides
Mucopolysaccharidosis VII (Sly's disease)	Course facies Depressed nasal bridge Large tongue	Hydrops fetalis Hepatomegaly	White cell/fibroblast βguccuonidase Note – GAGs are not always normal
Multiple sulphatase deficiency (Austin's variant)	Coarse facies depressed nasal bridge Large tongue	Ichthyosis Hepatomegaly Radiological changes Corneal clouding	White cell/fibroblast sulphatase (e.g., arylsulphatase A) Urinary GAGs
Mevalonate kinase deficiency	Abnormal facies	Hypotonia Hepatosplenomegaly Anaemia	Urinary organic acids
Menkes disease	Abnormal facies	Hypothermia Fine hair Tricchorrehixis nodosa Seizures	Serum copper and caeruloplasmin

GAGs = glycosaminoglycans

PURINE AND PYRIMIDINE DISORDERS

Purine and pyrimidines supply the basic components of DNA and RNA as well as important intracellular pools, e.g., ATP. Several inherited metabolic disorders of purine or pyrimidine metabolism have been described, affecting the functioning of the CNS, kidney and immune system and hence having a wide range of clinical presentations. The most severe disorder presenting in the neonatal period is xanthine oxidase/sulphite oxidase deficiency (molybdenum cofactor deficiency). The disorder presents with intractable seizures and can be suspected by the finding of a *low* plasma urate concentration and *low* urinary urate:creatinine ratio. Lesch-Nyhan syndrome can present, albeit rarely, in the neonatal period with characteristically *high* plasma and urinary urate concentrations.

Adenosine deaminase deficiency, associated with severe combined immune deficiency (SCID), manifests at birth with diarrhoea, failure to thrive and candidiasis.

THE DYSMORPHIC BABY AND INHERITED METABOLIC DISORDERS

Dysmorphic features in the newborn baby usually suggest an intrauterine insult, e.g., infection, drug exposure, chromosome abnormality or a genetic 'syndrome' without a known biochemical cause. In some cases, however, the malformation or dysmorphism can be associated with a biochemical disorder.

The neonate with dysmorphic features should have a careful and detailed examination to assess CNS function and should have chromosome analysis. Neurological and/or radiological abnormalities may suggest particular biochemical defects and the need for more specific tests (Table 6.2).

It is likely that an increasing number of syndromes will be found to have a biochemical basis and clinicians need to be aware of these possibilities and investigate accordingly.

FURTHER READING

Bennett MJ. The laboratory diagnosis of inborn errors of mitochondrial fatty acid oxidation. Ann Clin Biochem 1990; **27**: 519-531.

Clayton P, Thompson E. Dysmorphic syndromes with demonstrable biochemical abnormalities. J Med Genet 1988; **25**: 463-472.

Cleary MA, Wraith JE. Antenatal diagnosis of inborn errors of metabolism. Arch Dis Child 1991; **66**: 816-822.

Edwards MA, Grant S, Green A. A practical approach to the investigations of amino acid disorders. Ann Clin Biochem 1988; **25**: 129-141.

Fernandes J, Saudubray JM, Tada K, editors. Inborn Metabolic Diseases - Diagnosis and Treatment. Springer-Verlag, Berlin/Heidelberg, 1990.

Green A. When and how should we measure plasma ammonia? Ann Clin Biochem 1988; **25**: 199-209.

Green A. Inborn errors of organic acid metabolism. Br J Hosp Med 1989; **41**: 426-434.

Green A. Guide to diagnosis of inborn errors of metabolism in a District General Hospital. J Clin Path 1989; **42**: 84-91.

Holton JB. Diagnosis of inherited metabolic diseases in severely ill children. Ann Clin Biochem 1982; **19**: 389-395.

Holton JB, editor. Inherited Metabolic Diseases. Churchill Livingstone, Edinburgh, 1987.

Leonard JV. The early detection and management of inborn errors presenting acutely in the neonatal period. Eur J Paed 1985; **143**: 253-257.

Scholte HR, Busch HFM. Biochemical diagnosis and therapy of defects in oxidative phosphorylation. Ann Clin Biochem 1988; **25**: Suppl 27s-34s.

Scriver CR et al, editors. The Metabolic Basis of Inherited Disease, 6th edition. McGraw-Hill, 1989.

Wanders RJA, Heymans HSA, Schutgen RBH, Barth PG, van de Bosch H, Tager JM. Peroxisomal disorders in neurology. J Neur Sci 1988; **88**: 1-39

Wraith JE. Diagnosis and management of inborn errors of metabolism. Arch Dis Child 1989; **64**: 1410-1415.

Chapter 7

Drugs and the Neonate

DRUG ADMINISTRATION

ABSORPTION / ROUTE OF ADMINISTRATION

Liquid formulations of a variety of drugs can be administered to neonates. Variables such as rate of gastric emptying, acidity of gastric secretions, neonatal maturity or illness and the effects of milk on the drug itself means that this route produces unpredictable variability in drug absorption and hence in blood/tissue concentrations. Rectal administration of some drugs is more reliable and can be useful in some situations e.g., rectal theophylline for neonatal apnoea. There are practical problems with intramuscular injections, particularly the small amount of suitable skeletal muscle available to inject into in the small infant and the variability of tissue perfusion during illness.

Because of all these factors, most drugs given in the emergency situation or to babies in Neonatal Units, are given intravenously.

Significant systemic absorption can occur of substances applied locally to the skin and the eye. Systemic atropine-like side effects have been seen after cyclopentolate eyedrop administration and increased blood alcohol concentrations have been recorded in very immature babies after application of an alcoholic cleansing solution to the skin.

DISTRIBUTION

Neonates have a relatively larger total body water as compared with older children and adults, and a relatively larger proportion of that is extracellular fluid. In general, therefore, for most drugs which distribute within the extracellular space, a larger dose related to weight is needed in the neonate.

Extracellular fluid volume does correlate directly with body surface area, so there is an argument that drug dosage should be related directly to surface area rather than to weight. This presents practical difficulties, however, so weight criteria, along with gestational and postnatal ages, are usually employed.

Low total protein in neonatal plasma, together with particular characteristics of neonatal albumin, can lead to reduced drug protein binding in the neonate and a large apparent volume of distribution for drugs.

EFFECT OF BILIRUBIN

Bilirubin can compete with some drugs for albumin binding sites. The drug may displace bilirubin, leading to an increase in free bilirubin and a theoretically increased risk of kernicterus. This effect is important when considering the use of X-ray contrast media, indomethacin, some other anti-inflammatory agents, aspirin, or sulphonamides.

METABOLISM

Enzymatic biotransformation of drugs can be poor in the newborn, particularly in the pre-term neonate, leading to prolonged half-life of some drugs, and the need for therapeutic drug monitoring.

For example, pethidine is hydrolysed by an esterase which is present in low concentrations in newborn infants, and has a prolonged half-life of five hours or more. The hepatic cytochrome P450 system responsible for oxidation or reduction of drugs has an activity only 50% of that adults even at full term, however it is readily inducible e.g., by phenobarbitone. This may mean that the metabolism of concomitantly administered drugs is speeded up and levels may become subtherapeutic unless monitored closely. An example of this effect is provided by chloramphenicol, which should not generally be used in newborn infants unless therapeutic drug monitoring is performed.

Phenobarbitone and phenytoin themselves are hydroxylated relatively slowly. Diazepam is hydroxylated and conjugated poorly.

The N-demethylation path for theophylline and caffeine appears to be deficient in neonates, who have a specific methylation path, not present in adults, by which theophylline is largely converted to caffeine, which is excreted 85% unchanged.

The neonatal liver conjugates drugs poorly to glucuronides but has an enhanced sulphation pathway, e.g., in paracetamol metabolism. This can present problems when there is no compensatory pathway and drugs can accumulate to toxic levels. This problem occurred when chloramphenicol was first used in babies, and produced a fatal 'grey baby syndrome' with shock and peripheral circulatory collapse.

EXCRETION

Renal function is poor at birth, and poorer in the pre-term or sick neonate (Ch 2 and Ch 4). Glomerular filtration rate (GFR) can be as low as 2–3 mL / min in the 28 week baby, with only slow increase in the first postnatal week. After the first week, GFR increases more steeply and there is a sharp increase at the equivalent of 34 - 36 weeks gestation. This leads to very prolonged half-life ($T_{\frac{1}{2}}$) of some drugs e.g., digoxin $T_{\frac{1}{2}} = 30$ - 100h in the first week

Tubular function is poor particularly in the pre-term or sick baby and tubular secretion of drugs is diminished. For example, frusemide has a mean half-life of seven hours in the neonate with a consequently prolonged diuretic and natriuretic effect, in addition to producing calciuria and loss of other minerals.

Some antibacterial drugs e.g., gentamicin, are significantly affected by the low GFR and blood monitoring of trough and peak levels is essential. Concentrations must be rechecked regularly because of the reduction of drug half-life with increasing postnatal age.

ADVERSE EFFECTS OF DRUGS

Adverse effects are usually concentration-related, resulting from an exaggerated pharmacological response to the drugs. They are more common in neonates than in any other age group, because of all the variable factors noted above. Diarrhoea, electrolyte imbalance, hypoglycaemia, gastrointestinal bleeding, convulsions, hypotension, and tachycardia or bradycardia are all recognised side effects of drugs used in neonatal care.

Drug interactions may also produce adverse effects, e.g., by displacement of bilirubin by sulphonamide and induction of hepatic enzymes by phenobarbitone.

OBSTETRIC DRUGS AND THE NEONATE

Drugs administered to the mother may cross to the fetus and produce direct drug specific effects in the baby. This particularly applies to drugs which are rapidly absorbed across membranes, i.e., those of low molecular weight, low ionisation, and a high lipid: water partition ratio. High doses of barbiturates administered to the mother may produce respiratory depression in the baby at birth. High doses of benzodiazepines may lead to lethargy, hypotonia and poor temperature control. Narcotic analgesics given in labour may lead to neonatal respiratory depression which is dose related e.g., pethidine, alfentanyl.

Intravenous naloxone given to the baby at birth will reverse narcotic-induced effects within 1-2 minutes, but has a duration of action of only 1-2 hours. This may be shorter than the duration of action of pethidine, so supplementary i.m. naloxone should be given.

Anaesthetic drugs given to the mother before delivery may also have an indirect effect by producing fetal distress or asphyxia, the treatment of which is the restoration of perfusion and gas exchange. Inhalational agents will only affect the baby if high doses are used or if the induction delivery interval is prolonged (>20 minutes).

DRUGS AND BREAST MILK

Many drugs given to the mother postnatally will be excreted to some degree in the milk, though the amount available for absorption by the baby is usually small (<2% of maternal dose). In the vast majority of cases, the risk to the neonate is minimal, and breast feeding is not contraindicated. There are very few situations in which it is absolutely contraindicated. Some of these are shown in Table 7.1. A complete current list is available in the British National Formulary Appendix.

Drugs given to the mother may sometimes have a direct undesirable effect on the baby e.g., purgatives; breast feeding should be delayed until the drug effect is complete. In some cases, the potential effect of a drug on the baby can be monitored by performing the relevant blood test, for example antithyroid drugs given in the management of maternal thyrotoxicosis, can suppress thyroid function in the breast-fed infant.

Table 7.1   Maternal drugs for which breast feeding is contraindicated

• Lithium	• Cytotoxic drugs
• Immunosuppressants (not steroids)	• Radiopharmaceuticals
• Phenindione	• Ergot alkaloids

DRUG WITHDRAWAL

Maternal drug addiction, particularly to narcotic agents, may lead to the development of a withdrawal syndrome in the neonate after delivery. Presentation is usually within four days of birth, but can be delayed until ten days and may last up to six months.

Symptoms and signs are variable, and are predominantly those of autonomic overactivity and cerebral irritability. Nasal congestion, sneezing, yawning, runny eyes, photophobia, poor suck, hiccups and diarrhoea have all been described. In more severe cases there is an abnormal high-pitched cry, increased extensor tone, irritability, poor sleeping, tachypnoea, weight loss and convulsions.

Treatment is symptomatic; chlorpromazine is among the most useful of the sedative drugs employed.

THERAPEUTIC MONITORING

Drugs with unpredictable half-life, drugs with toxic cumulative effects, drugs with a narrow therapeutic index (difference between effective and toxic levels), and drugs in which inadequate dosage leads to loss of efficacy, all require regular monitoring of blood levels in the neonate.

A list of such drugs and their therapeutic ranges in plasma is given in Table 7.2.

Table 7.2   Therapeutic monitoring of drugs in neonates

Drugs	Sampling time	Range
Amikacin	peak trough	15-20mg/L <4mg/L
Gentamicin	peak trough	4-10mg/L <2mg/L
Vancomycin	peak trough	18-25mg/L <10mg/L
Chloramphenicol	peak	15-25mg/L
Caffeine	>6h post dose	15-30mg/L
Theophylline	peak	5-12mg/L
Phenobarbitone	>6h post dose	15-30mg/L
Phenytoin	>8h post dose	10-20mg/L
Digoxin	>6h post dose	1-2µg/L

FURTHER READING

Appendix 5: Breast-feeding. British National Formulary 1993; (No.25). British Medical Association and the Royal Pharmaceutical Society of Great Britain.

Grant E, Golightly P. Drugs in breast feeding. Prescribers' Journal 1992; **32** (Pt 3): 90-9.

Chapter 8

Parenteral Nutrition in the Neonate

INTRODUCTION

Intravenous feeding has been an important development in promoting the survival of the pre-term and low birth weight infant as well as infants born at term with compromised gastrointestinal function. It is a skilled procedure and should only be undertaken by experienced medical and nursing staff with adequate specialist support. In our experience it is best provided on a 'team' basis with regular involvement of an experienced clinician, dietitian, pharmacist, biochemist, nurse and microbiologist.

INDICATIONS FOR PARENTERAL NUTRITION (PN)

Whenever possible nutrition should be maintained enterally, e.g., by the nasogastric route in the pre-term infant, or via duodenal or jejunal tube feeding in the surgical infant. If the gastrointestinal tract is compromised and it is judged that the neonate will be unable to absorb sufficient nutrients to prevent catabolism, then parenteral, that is, intravenous, feeding should be considered. Absolute indications include extreme immaturity, intestinal obstruction or necrotising enterocolitis. In some neonatal units, ventilated infants are not offered enteral feeding and so require parenteral nutrition.

The neonate who has had gut resection (e.g., for duodenal or ileal atresia) is a particular candidate for parenteral nutrition.

The pre-term infant has very little stored energy resources (i.e., glycogen and fat); at 28 weeks gestation virtually all of the carbohydrate, fat and protein is structural. Failure to supply adequate nutrition to the low birth weight baby will result in a catabolic state and tissue breakdown will ensue rapidly. It may be impossible to ensure adequate nutrient intake enterally without the risk of overloading the gut and consequent diarrhoea or regurgitation and aspiration pneumonia.

The decision to start PN in this situation is therefore based on how much enteral feed the baby can take and whether there are any additional stress factors, e.g., sepsis, respiratory difficulties or severe intra-uterine growth retardation. In the term infant an intake of at least 110kcal/kg/24h is required to promote anabolism. Recommended 24 hourly inputs are: protein, 2.5g/kg; fat, 3g/kg, and carbohydrate, 14g/kg. In the pre-term infant, growth may be possible on a significantly lower caloric intake than this.

PRACTICAL ASPECTS OF PARENTERAL FEEDING

NUTRIENT SOURCES AND THE COMPOSITION OF INTRAVENOUS SOLUTIONS

Requirements for parenteral nutrition formulae are based on data from normal enterally fed babies and regimes have been developed to take account of the differing needs of the term or pre-term baby. Commercial amino acid preparations (Vaminolact, Preamine) suitable for the neonate are available and can be used as the basis for the preparation of a nutritionally complete regime. This needs to contain:

Carbohydrate	Glucose is the carbohydrate of choice and in practice regimes containing other substrates (e.g., fructose) are not recommended and are rarely used.
Lipid	Parenteral lipid emulsions (e.g., Intralipid) are isotonic solutions which provide essential fatty acids and are energy rich. They are metabolised in the same way as chylomicrons. Parenteral lipid should be introduced gradually, particularly in babies who are pre-term or small for gestation, and in those with jaundice or liver dysfunction.
Nitrogen	A balanced mixture of L-amino acids (including adequate essential amino acids) is required. Formulae particularly suited for pre-term babies are available. Taurine is essential in very low birth weight infants.

Vitamins	Water soluble and fat soluble preparations are given in doses appropriate to the baby's weight
Minerals	Only small amounts of sodium and potassium are provided in commercial amino acid solutions and supplements of sodium and potassium chloride are required to meet the basic requirements. Calcium, magnesium and phosphate supplements are also required to fulfill the basic requirements.
	Pre-term infants require additional phosphate supplementation (see Ch 4).
Trace elements	These are provided as a supplement based on body weight.

The limited solubility of the inorganic salts of calcium and phosphate may makeprovision of the full requirements impossible, particularly in the pre-term infant. Recently the greater solubility of glucose 1-phosphate and calcium glycerophosphate have been used to increase the calcium and phosphate concentrations of intravenous feeding solutions.

The volume and nutrient content of the feed is increased gradually over about six days, particularly with regard to the protein and lipid content. For details of intravenous regimens and practicality of administration, the reader is referred to the texts mentioned at the end of this section.

METABOLIC COMPLICATIONS
The metabolic complications of PN are summarised in table 8.1.

Hyperglycaemia and glycosuria (>0.5%) may occur in very low birth weight babies and 6 hourly BM Stix monitoring and urine testing is recommended. An insulin infusion may be used to control blood glucose and may also lead to an improvement in weight gain. Hyperglycaemia in a term infant or a previously stable infant is uncommon and when it occurs is suggestive of infection or heart failure.

Hypercholesterolaemia has been noted in some babies receiving Intralipid. The phospholipid present as an emulsifier has been implicated as the cause of this hypercholesterolaemia and its intake can be reduced by giving the Intralipid as a 20% rather than a 10% emulsion. The significance of this hypercholesterolaemia

Table 8.1   Metabolic complications of parenteral nutrition in neonates

Frequent complications	Less frequent complications
*Sodium depletion	*Hyperphenylalaninaemia (± hypertyrosinaemia)
*Potassium depletion	*Hyperlipidaemia (Cholesterol↑ Triglycerides↑)
*Hyperglycaemia	Zinc deficiency
*Glycosuria	Copper deficiency
*Jaundice	Selenium deficiency
*Hypophosphataemia	Hyperammonaemia
Metabolic acidosis	
Calcium depletion	

*particularly important in extreme pre-term infants (see Ch 4)

is not known but it is probably best avoided. Hypercholesterolaemia may not be a complication when Lipofundin, an alternative lipid source with 50% long chain triglycerides and 50% medium chain triglycerides, is used. Hypertriglyceridaemia should not occur if the rate of lipid infusion is controlled appropriately.

Hyperbilirubinaemia occurs in some neonates particularly if on PN for more than 14 days. The cause of the jaundice is probably multifactorial with enteral starvation being an important component. Free fatty acids in the blood displace bilirubin from albumin and may increase the risk of kernicterus. It is therefore recommended that lipid emulsions should not be given if plasma bilirubin exceeds 170 μmol/L and the dose should be reduced at bilirubin concentrations between 100 and 170 μmol/L. Intrahepatic cholestasis has been reported as a complication of prolonged parenteral nutrition by some, but in our experience is uncommon. Both a complete absence of any enteral feeding and systemic infection may increase the likelihood of cholestasis.

Amino acid imbalances have been observed over many years with the use of a variety of products formulated primarily for administration to adult patients. With the advent of newer products, (e.g., Vaminolact) whose formulae are based on breast milk and hence specifically tailored for the premature/low birth weight baby, there is now much less of a problem. The absence of taurine in some formulae has been associated with low plasma taurine concentrations and a reversible abnormality in the electroretinogram in patients on long term therapy and is still cause for concern.

There have been several reports of hyperphenylalaninaemia in babies receiving Vamin (an amino acid solution widely used in adult PN). Vamin contains more than twice as much phenylalanine as breast milk and the specially adapted infant formulae. It is therefore advisable to monitor plasma amino acids; a qualitative procedure (e.g., one-dimensional thin layer chromatography) is adequate. This should be done when the *full* i.v. regime has been given for three days. If the phenylalanine is normal and the baby remains stable, then repeat monitoring is not indicated.

Hyperammonaemia is a rare complication with the currently available nitrogen sources and if liver function is normal. If, however, the baby becomes lethargic or develops fits then plasma ammonia concentration should be measured.

Mild acid base disturbances are common, particularly as PN proceeds. Such findings are rarely associated with any clinical symptoms and unless the base deficit exceeds minus 5mmol/L, are generally safely ignored. Lactic acidosis has been reported in paediatric patients with cancer receiving total parenteral nutrition.

Electrolyte abnormalities e.g., hyponatraemia, hypokalaemia and hypocalcaemia, frequently occur in this clinical group as a result of their primary disorder, whether or not they receive PN. Neonates with continuing abnormal fluid and electrolyte losses, e.g., diarrhoea, upper gastrointestinal fluid loss or renal losses, are particularly prone to electrolyte depletion and require regular monitoring of plasma sodium, potassium and calcium concentrations. If hypocalcaemia occurs, the albumin should be checked and magnesium should be measured if there is refractory hypocalcaemia.

Hypophosphataemia is one of the commonest abnormalities arising from PN and regular measurement of plasma phosphate is essential. Increased phosphate provision may be required because of excess losses from the gastrointestinal tract or because of the bone disease of premature infants (see Ch 4, p 70).

Plasma selenium and zinc concentrations tend to fall as the duration of PN increases and deficiency may occur during long term PN. A falling plasma alkaline phosphatase activity may be a clue to zinc deficiency. If PN is prolonged, i.e., more than three weeks, then zinc, copper and selenium should be measured.

Some elements may be given in excess of requirements unintentionally, as contaminants, particularly of amino acid solutions. Aluminium accumulation has been implicated as a contributor to metabolic bone disease in infants, although there is no evidence that formulae in current use pose a problem.

BIOCHEMICAL MONITORING OF PARENTERAL NUTRITION

There are numerous guidelines to biochemical monitoring, most of them based on little hard scientific data. With increasing experience and availability of more appropriate products for the baby, worries about potential biochemical complications have reduced and reported complications are now uncommon.

Unnecessary blood sampling is traumatic to the baby and creates an added risk of infection and anaemia. Our experience suggests that for those infants who arebeing monitored *solely* because they are receiving parenteral nutrition, a

Table 8.2   Protocol for routine biochemical/haematological monitoring of term neonates on PN

Timing	Body fluid	Tests
Pre-PN	Blood/plasma	Sodium, potassium, bilirubin, phosphate
	Urine	Sodium, potassium
After 3 days or more full PN	Plasma	Amino acids (qualitative)
Each week of PN	Blood/plasma	Sodium, potassium— twice weekly Phosphate, bilirubin — once weekly Glucose (BM Stix) — daily first week or more frequently if unstable or preterm. Haemoglobin, haemotocrit, WBC and differential and platelets.
Additional tests after 2 weeks PN	Blood/plasma	Calcium, alkaline phosphatase— then weekly.
	Urine	Sodium, potassium
Additional tests after 3 weeks PN	Blood	Selenium, zinc, copper— then every three weeks.

NOTES

1. Preterm infants will require additional monitoring, particularly plasma phosphate and glucose and urine glucose (Clinistix).
2. More frequent phosphate monitoring will be required if phosphate is low.
3. 'Apparently' low glucose results by BM Stix (i.e., <2mmol/L) *must* be confirmed with a laboratory result)
4. Frequency of glucose monitoring can be reduced after first week unless glucose intake is being increased or baby is preterm.

conservative approach to monitoring can be recommended (Table 8.2). However, in an infant who is clinically unstable, has major organ failure or has unusual losses, more frequent or extensive monitoring may be needed. It may also be needed in the premature infant, though in practice what can be achieved may be limited by their low blood volume and the consequently small specimen sizes.

The timing of blood collections should be standardised so that blood is collected after the lipid infusion has been turned off for four hours. Blood taken during or soon after stopping the lipid infusion may be artefactually lipaemic and produce spurious results. If there is particular concern about lipid clearance, e.g., due to liver dysfunction, plasma triglyceride and free fatty acid concentrations should be measured; visual lipaemia provides an insensitive assessment and does not correlate well with quantitative measurements. In babies with no particular reason for acid base disturbances, routine hydrogen ion and blood gas measurements are not indicated. Osmolality measurements are not included in our protocol as in our experience they add little if anything to management. It is usually more informative to measure individual analytes.

FURTHER READING

Bell PA, Booth IW, Puntis JWL. Paediatric Parenteral Nutrition. Kabi Vitrum Ltd, 1990.

Hay Jr. WW, editor. Neonatal Nutrition and Metabolism. Mosby Year Book, St. Louis, 1991.

Heird WD, Parental feeding. In:

Effective care of the newborn infant. Sinclair JC and Bracken MB Eds. Oxford Medical Publications, 1992; 141-160.

Insley J, editor. Parenteral nutrition in the neonate. In:

A Paediatric Vade Mecum, 12th edition, Edward Arnold, London, 1990.

Chapter 9

Acid Base Homeostasis and its Disorders

ACID BASE STATUS IN THE FETUS

The fetus is at risk of hypoxia and resultant acidosis if there is poor placental circulation or interruption to it prior to delivery. The growth retarded fetus is at particular risk of acidosis. Harmful effects of acidosis include periventricular haemorrhage, leucomalacia, increased vascular resistance and reduced myocardial function. During labour, hypoxia can result from oxytocin-induced contractions or episodes of umbilical cord occlusion due to compression or entanglement around the fetus. If severe intrauterine asphyxia persists, with resultant ischaemia to the organs, then permanent damage can result, in particular to the CNS, even though the baby may subsequently be successfully resuscitated (Fig 9.1).

ACID BASE STATUS DURING DELIVERY AND AT BIRTH

Asphyxia before birth leads to anaerobic metabolism in the fetus and the production of lactic acid. pH, therefore, can provide a crude index of the severity of the asphyxial process at a particular point in time during labour. This information can aid decision making about whether to expedite delivery — for instance by performing an emergency caesarian section. Fetal pH is usually measured in a capillary blood specimen obtained from the baby's scalp. The procedure involves making a nick in the scalp with a metal blade and collecting blood through a long glass capillary tube, inserted through the cervix. The commonest clinical indication for a fetal scalp pH measurement would be a change in the cardiotocograph (CTG) or fetal heart tracing indicating possible fetal distress. Such changes are loss of variability in the trace, sustained fetal tachycardia or dips in the fetal heart rate which do not recover in time with the end of each contraction (Type 2 dips).

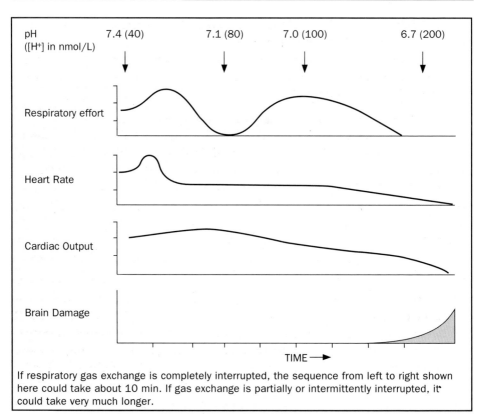

| pH ([H⁺] in nmol/L) | 7.4 (40) | 7.1 (80) | 7.0 (100) | 6.7 (200) |

Respiratory effort

Heart Rate

Cardiac Output

Brain Damage

TIME ⟶

If respiratory gas exchange is completely interrupted, the sequence from left to right shown here could take about 10 min. If gas exchange is partially or intermittently interrupted, it could take very much longer.

Fig 9.1   Sequence of events in birth asphyxia

A pH measurement, obtained in this way, of greater than 7.25 is generally taken as an indication that fetal health is not in imminent danger; a value of 7.20 to 7.25 as warranting close observation and a repeat measurement, and a level of less than 7.20 as indicating a need for immediate delivery, either vaginally or by caesarian section.

The asphyxiated infant is unlikely to breathe normally after delivery. Gasping irregular respirations will lead to rapid improvements in and reversal of the physiological effects of asphyxia due to the increase in the baby's PO_2 to concentrations above those of the fetus, even when breathing room air. This process can be accelerated by giving the baby oxygen- enriched air by mask.

If the baby has sustained severe or prolonged asphyxia, he may be apnoeic and shocked, with a bradycardia (possibly severe), pallor and circulatory collapse. In this state, active ventilation must be achieved by the resuscitator to inflate the baby's lungs and begin to reverse the asphyxial process. This can be done using a mask, an endotracheal tube and positive pressure ventilation, or, in an emergency, modified 'mouth to mouth' resuscitation bearing in mind the low pressures required and the size of the baby.

The physiology of resuscitation is essentially a reversal of the pathophysiology of asphyxia. If asphyxia has reached the stage of cardiac failure, restoration of cardiac output by external massage may be necessary in addition to inflation of the lungs. This seldom occurs unless the pH has fallen below 6.9. With re-oxygenation, and reversal of acidosis (which may be aided by administration of sodium bicarbonate through the umbilical vein) the myocardium rapidly responds, and circulation is restored. Transient hypertension will follow, due to vasoconstriction of non-vital organs, then pressures will fall towards normal. The base deficit may actually increase at this stage as lactic acid produced in peripheral tissues enters the main circulation.

Spontaneous respiration returns as the asphyxia recovers. The time taken for this to occur is a crude indication of the severity of the acute asphyxial insult and likely long-term clinical consequences. Babies who have had an extremely low pH at delivery, but who establish normal respiration after ten minutes, are usually free from brain damage. Babies who have not established respiration by twenty minutes, despite full and adequate resuscitation, form an extremely high risk group with increased mortality and morbidity in the form of spastic cerebral palsy.

During the recovery phase of asphyxia, several transient metabolic abnormalities may become evident. These include hypoglycaemia, due to depletion of carbohydrate reserves, and hypocalcaemia. Severe asphyxia may damage renal function and may produce renal failure of variable degree.

ACID BASE STATUS IN THE NEONATE

Acid base control in the neonate is dependent upon adequate respiration and perfusion and intact renal and hepatic function. The neonate is particularly vulnerable to disturbances of acid base balance because of the relative immaturity of the organ systems. This is exacerbated in the premature infant and/or if there is superimposed organ dysfunction, e.g., intrinsic renal disease, or dysfunction secondary to poor perfusion or infection.

RESPIRATORY CAUSES OF ACID-BASE DISTURBANCES

Urgent management of respiratory failure in the newborn infant is of paramount importance. Hypoxic ischaemic encephalopathy is the commonest cause of perinatally acquired brain damage in the term baby, although only a minority of cases of hypoxic-ischaemic damage arise during labour. Seventy percent of newborns requiring resuscitation arise from a predictable high risk group. The remainder however are delivered after an apparently normal labour with no evidence of fetal compromise and delayed respiration or failure to become pink in these cases is due to other causes (Table 9.1a and b).

Drugs used as maternal analgesics, sedatives or general anaesthetics during labour, will cross the placenta and can depress the fetal respiratory centre. In practice respiratory depression from drugs is likely to be important only in premature infants or those with asphyxia superimposed from other causes (see Ch 7).

The premature infant often requires active resuscitation. The causation of respiratory failure in this group is multifactorial, including asphyxia, drugs, and the difficulty of establishing respiration with stiff, surfactant-deficient lungs (see Ch4, p 67). Avoidance of perinatal hypoxia is particularly important because of the association of hypoxia with more severe surfactant deficiency, and with intraventricular haemorrhage and periventricular leucomalacia. Infants with established surfactant deficiency usually have a respiratory acidosis initially, due to carbon dioxide retention. Underventilation may be due to inadequate respiratory effort, irregular respiration, or muscle weakness. When hypoxia ensues and if respiratory management is inadequate, the acidosis is compounded by a metabolic component, due to increased lactate production from anaerobic

Table 9.1   Causes of delayed respiration and persistent cyanosis in the neonate

(a) Causes of delayed respiration	(b) Causes of persistent cyanosis
• Intrapartum asphyxia	• Persistent pulmonary hypertension
• Drugs (causing CNS depression)	• Cyanotic congenital heart defect
• Prematurity	• Underexpansion of lungs (surfactant deficiency)
• Trauma to CNS	
• Congenital abnormalities	• Pneumothorax
• Anaemia/blood loss	• Diaphragmatic hernia
• Muscle weakness (prematurity or primary muscle disease)	• Anatomical abnormality of airways

metabolism. It is important that these disturbances are minimised by providing appropriate ventilatory support for the baby and maintaining adequate oxygenation.

NON-RESPIRATORY CAUSES OF ACID BASE DISTURBANCES

RENAL DYSFUNCTION

Primary renal dysfunction may lead to inability to excrete an acid load and hence metabolic acidosis, e.g., renal tubular acidosis (Ch 3, p 55). If there is a major degree of acidosis, the baby will attempt to compensate by hyperventilation, and PCO_2 will be reduced.

Secondary or transient renal dysfunction, for instance following birth asphyxia, may also lead to acidosis but this does not usually cause a problem in clinical management.

Pre-term babies may develop a chronic, mild, metabolic acidosis due to renal immaturity and inability to excrete the physiologically generated acid load. This may be exacerbated by the use of parenteral nutrition, and total nitrogen intake may have to be reduced temporarily in this case.

HYPOPERFUSION

The commonest acidosis in the newborn is lactic acidosis due to poor perfusion. There are numerous causes including structural abnormalities, e.g., hypoplastic left heart, as well as sepsis, necrotising enterocolitis and loss of blood.

OVERPRODUCTION OF ACID

Severe metabolic acidosis, with compensatory respiratory alkalosis, will occur in babies with a whole range of inherited defects of organic acid metabolism (see Ch 6). In these situations acidosis is not present at birth but will usually occur within 24-72h, often presenting as tachypnoea in a previously well baby. Blood pH may be normal due to the presence of a compensatory respiratory alkalosis.

ACID BASE ASSESSMENT

COLLECTION AND TRANSPORT OF BLOOD

It is extremely important to pay attention to the quality of specimen obtained for acid base monitoring. The best specimens are arterial, collected through an indwelling catheter with minimal disturbance to the infant. In many cases however capillary blood is used. In such situations it is essential that the person collecting the blood has been properly trained to collect these specimens. The blood must be free flowing from a well perfused limb and collected into the special heparinised capillary tubes designed for blood gas analysis. Great care must be taken to ensure that air bubbles are not trapped in the tube, and if the blood gas analyser is in a remote site, that there is appropriate storage of the blood at 4°C during transit. Capillary blood is *not* suitable for PO_2 measurement. Arterial 'stab' samples are often used to provide an instantaneous assessment of blood gas status. However, the disturbance and pain involved commonly make the infant either apnoeic or cyanosed, rendering the sample considerably less useful.

BLOOD GAS ANALYSIS

There are several blood gas analysers which are suitable for use for neonates. Small sample size and ease for use with capillary tubes or syringes are obviously key factors when choosing an instrument.

In units with their own blood gas analyser where non-laboratory clinical staff are trained to use the instruments, it is imperative that there is an appropriate quality assurance programme, maintenance programme, and support for training and troubleshooting provided from the laboratory. This must include provision of a designated 'back up' instrument which may be most appropriately located in the main laboratory.

CONTINUOUS GAS MONITORING

TRANSCUTANEOUS GAS ANALYSIS

Blood gas analysis of arterial specimens give measurements of PO_2, pH and PCO_2 at a particular time. In the sick neonate, however, PO_2 particularly may be extremely variable, with profound falls after handling procedures, such as physiotherapy or suction, or respiratory irregularity. A fall in PO_2 may also provide early warning of significant clinical problems – for instance, pneumothorax, or air leak, in a baby with respiratory distress syndrome – before this could be detected by observing changes in colour, heart rate, or respiration. Because of these factors, some form of continuous PO_2 monitoring or, alternatively, oxygen saturation monitoring, is usually employed in the care of the baby receiving oxygen. This can reveal trends and facilitate rapid intervention when necessary.

For these reasons electrodes for the transcutaneous measurement of oxygen tension ($TcPO_2$) are widely used in Neonatal Units.

Problems of $TcPO_2$ Monitoring

While these electrodes are extremely useful in monitoring arterial PO_2 non-invasively, there are problems. The electrode is heated to 43°C and may cause first or second degree burning of the skin, especially in the poorly-perfused or very immature baby. On occasions, unexpected discrepancies can arise between transcutaneous and arterial PO_2, necessitating correlation with direct arterial samples at frequent intervals. If a baby is shocked and poorly perfused, it may be impossible to obtain a $TcPO_2$ reading. Over a period of hours, 'electrode drift' will occur, and re-zeroing and recalibration of electrodes must be performed 4-6 hourly.

In older babies, particularly those with chronic lung disease who have received steroids, the skin and subcutaneous tissue characteristics are altered and it is not possible to obtain accurate or consistent $TcPO_2$ measurements.

The $TcPO_2$ probe should be cross-checked for accuracy by comparing its reading with four-hourly or more frequent arterial PO_2 measurements taken from an indwelling catheter. In some units, $TcPO_2$ is relied on alone, without such correlation; this is bad clinical practice and should be discouraged.

OXYGEN SATURATION MONITORING (PULSE OXIMETRY)

Oxygen is present in the blood in two physical forms:

- freely dissolved in plasma water
- bound reversibly to haemoglobin within red cells

The first of these is directly related to the partial pressure of oxygen in blood (PO_2). This accounts for about 2% of total blood oxygen content.

The other 98% is the oxygen bound to haemoglobin. This is also related to PO_2 and the relationship is defined by the oxygen-haemoglobin affinity curve. This can be graphically represented as a comparison between the percentage of haemoglobin fully saturated with oxygen ($[HbO_2]/[Hb]+[HbO_2]$) ×100 and blood PO_2. In the neonate, this curve will tend to be shifted to the left because of the characteristics of neonatal red cells (Fig 9.2).

Oxygen carrying capacity will depend on the haemoglobin concentration (which falls in the first weeks of postnatal life). During this period, however, the

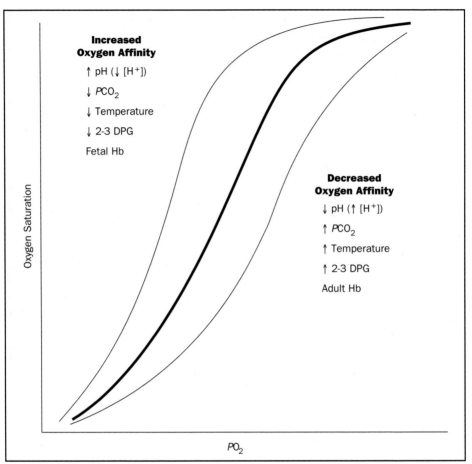

Increased Oxygen Affinity

↑ pH (↓ [H⁺])

↓ PCO_2

↓ Temperature

↓ 2-3 DPG

Fetal Hb

Decreased Oxygen Affinity

↓ pH (↑ [H⁺])

↑ PCO_2

↑ Temperature

↑ 2-3 DPG

Adult Hb

Oxygen Saturation

PO_2

Fig 9.2   Factors affecting oxygen-haemoglobin affinity in the neonate

proportion of fetal haemoglobin falls, and the oxygen released to tissue (Fig 9.3, hatched areas) increases. The hatched area shown displays the volume of oxygen released as the PO_2 falls from a point at which haemoglobin is 95% saturated to an approximate tissue PO_2 of 5.3 kPa.

Direct measurement of the percentage of haemoglobin saturated with oxygen may be of theoretical as well as practical value. It provides an indication of the adequacy of tissue oxygen supply. This will be compromised if oxygen saturation (SaO_2) is less than 80%

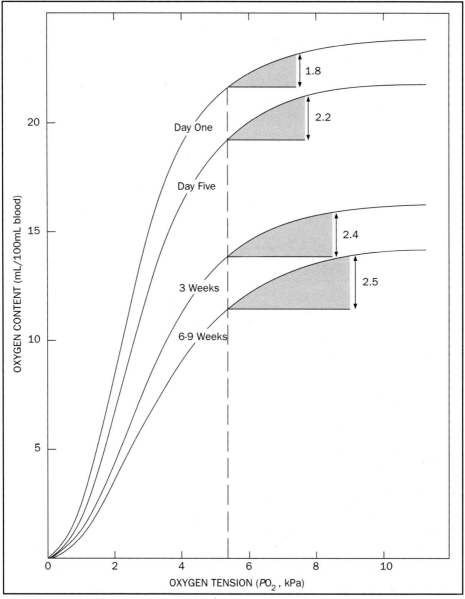

Fig 9.3 Relationship between blood oxygen content and PO_2 at different ages in normal term infants

Pulse oximetry, which uses a light-emitting probe attached to a hand or foot, can achieve this. Saturation is computed by microprocessor from the light absorption characteristics of the pulsatile flow (containing both oxygenated and non-oxygenated haemoglobin) as it passes beneath the probe. The results correlate closely with validated arterial saturation measurements in some oximeters (e.g., Nellcor) but there is variability between results obtained with some other instruments.

Rapidly responding saturation results can be obtained without initial calibration. They are obtainable in poorly perfused babies and in older babies with chronic oxygen dependency. No re-calibration of probes during use is required.

However, since the normal levels of SaO_2 in the neonate are 95%-98%, hyperoxaemia may occur undetected unless PO_2 is also known. This is because only small changes in SaO_2 occur even with large alterations in partial pressure of oxygen at this upper end of the dissociation curve.

Pulmonary circulation, ductus arteriosus diameter, and cellular and tissue injury from oxygen free radical production all relate to PO_2 rather than to oxygen content. Knowledge of PO_2 is therefore vital when oxygen saturation monitoring is being used in the acutely ill nenonate.

INTRAVASCULAR PO_2 ELECTRODES
Umbilical artery catheters are available which have an intrinsic PO_2 electrode at their tip (Orange Medical). This can then usefully provide continuous PO_2 data for as long as the umbilical catheter remains *in situ*. Regular recalibration of the system against directly measured arterial PO_2 remains essential.

Table 9.2 Arterial blood gas values in normal full term neonates

	pH	[H⁺] (mean)	PCO_2	PO_2
Umbilical vein	7.32 (0.06)	48	5.04 (0.75)	3.65 (0.76)
Umbilical artery	7.24 (0.06)	58	6.55 (0.77)	2.12 (0.51)
Arterial — 1 hour	7.33 (0.03)	47	4.81 (0.56)	8.44 (1.51)
Arterial — 24 hours	7.37 (0.03)	43	4.45 (0.41)	9.69 (1.27)
Arterial — 7 days	7.37 (0.03)	43	4.79 (0.41)	9.74 (1.30)

INTERPRETATION

Reference values for blood gases in normal full term neonates, are shown in Table 9.2. Interpretation of acid base measurements must take into account the type of specimen (capillary/arterial), the clinical state and results of other relevant investigations. A base excess of lower than minus 4mmol/L is abnormal although in practice further investigation is not usually undertaken until it falls to below minus 8mmol/L.

Table 9.3   Causes of acid base disturbance in the neonate

	pH	[H⁺]	PCO_2	[HCO₃⁻]	Causes
Respiratory Acidosis	↓	↑	↑	↑	Hypoventilation
Respiratory Alkalosis	↓	↑	↑	↑	Overventilation Hyperammonaemia
Metabolic Acidosis	↓	↑	N/↓	↑	Renal impairment Poor perfusion Loss of fluid from gastrointestinal tract Metabolic disorders
Metabolic Alkalosis	↓	↑	N/↑	↑	Bicarbonate administration Pyloric stenosis Hypokalaemia

DIFFERENTIAL DIAGNOSIS OF ACID BASE DISTURBANCES (see Tables 9.3 and 9.4)

ACIDOSIS

The commonest causes of acidosis in the neonate are hypoxia and poor tissue perfusion which may derive from birth asphyxia or later illness. The infant with an infection is particularly likely to be acidotic due to poor perfusion and overproduction of hydrogen ions.

Metabolic acidosis in neonates due to renal disease may be due to renal failure or renal tubular acidosis (RTA) (see p 55). The commonest cause of renal failure is poor renal perfusion during asphyxia; it is usually reversible and only conservative methods of management are required. If plasma creatinine is normal and there is hyperchloraemia with metabolic acidosis, then RTA is probable. There is a whole range of metabolic disorders (see Ch 6, p 109) which cause metabolic acidosis, the commonest being methylmalonic acidaemia, propionic acidaemia and lactic acidosis.

Table 9.4   Differential diagnosis of acidosis

Cause	Supporting Evidence
Circulatory	↑Plasma lactate, ↑Anion gap, ↓Blood pressure
Renal	N/↑Creatinine, ↑Chloride, N/↑Urine pH, Normal anion gap
Respiratory	Clinical signs, ↑PCO_2
Metabolic	↑Anion gap, +ve Urinary ketones, N/↓ Urine pH

Differential diagnosis of metabolic acidosis may be aided by calculation of the plasma anion gap $\{([Na^+]+[K^+])-([HCO_3^-]+[Cl^-])\}$.

A gap of greater than 20mmol/L is suggestive of an organic acid disorder (p 109) or lactic acidosis due to hypoxia. Biochemical investigations which may help with the differential diagnosis are urinary ketones, plasma glucose, ammonia and lactate concentrations, urine and plasma amino acids and urinary organic acids. If plasma chloride concentration is increased, with normal amino acids and organic acids, then renal tubular disease should be considered.

ALKALOSIS

The commonest cause of alkalosis is iatrogenic respiratory alkalosis in ventilated babies. Excess administration of bicarbonate can also produce alkalosis when acidosis has been overestimated clinically.

MANAGEMENT OF ACID BASE DISTURBANCES IN THE NEONATE

All sick babies, particularly if there is clinical evidence of poor perfusion, respiratory insufficiency, dehydration or infection, should have their acid base status assessed. Guides to the management of the pre-term baby with respiratory distress syndrome and of the term baby with cyanosis are outlined in Figs 9.4 and 9.5 respectively.

HYPOXAEMIA

The normal arterial PO_2 for a term baby breathing air is 8-11kPa. A PO_2 below 2-3kPa will cause metabolic acidosis due to anaerobic metabolism and demands *urgent* attention.

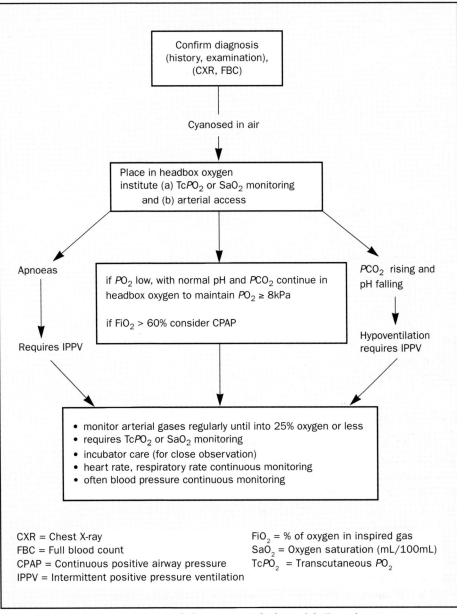

Fig 9.4 Initial management of the preterm baby with Respiratory Distress Syndrome

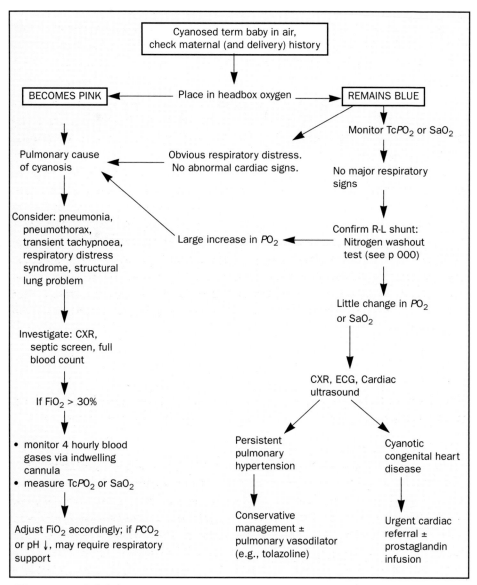

Fig 9.5   Initial management of cyanosis in the term baby

A reduced PO_2 may be due to pulmonary disease, failure of circulatory adaptation at birth (persistent pulmonary hypertension) or an anatomical by-pass of the pulmonary circulation. It is important to diagnose an anatomical cause so that corrective surgery can be undertaken if appropriate. Most pulmonary causes ofhypoxia can be differentiated by a combination of history, examination, chest X-ray, and bacteriological investigation.

In the severely hypoxaemic baby, the 'Nitrogen washout' test is used to separate the pulmonary causes from the failure of adaptation or 'by-pass' causes. The procedure is first to measure the PO_2 from the right radial artery or to determine the oxygen saturation in the right arm (i.e., pre-ductal part of the circulation) using a pulse oximeter. The baby is then placed into as near to 100% oxygen as practical, using a headbox. In hypoxia of pulmonary origin, there will be a very large increase in PO_2 or SaO_2 resulting from this manoeuvre. In pulmonary by-pass, there may be an increase of 1-2kPa at most and the baby will remain significantly hypoxic. Cardiac ultrasound examination will define structural abnormality. If the heart is structurally normal and the lungs clear on chest X-ray, the baby probably has persistent pulmonary hypertension. This represents failure of pulmonary vasodilation at birth and can arise *de novo* or after asphyxia. Pulmonary vasodilators usually lead to steady improvement within the first week.

HYPEROXAEMIA

OXYGEN TOXICITY
Particularly in the immature infant, excess oxygen carries significant hazards. The most major ones are lung toxicity and retinopathy of prematurity.

Pulmonary Toxicity
This is related to the concentration of inspired oxygen, and is a significant risk if a baby receives oxygen concentrations of 80% or more over a period of more than a few hours. Bronchopulmonary dysplasia, recognised as a severe complication following idiopathic respiratory distress syndrome in babies who have received mechanical ventilation, has many histopathological features in common with those produced by oxygen toxicity in animals. The earliest changes resemble exaggerated normal repair processes in the bronchiolar walls. The lungs become solid. Oedema around the bronchioles develops together with fibroblastic proliferation. Foci of distorted proliferated capillaries are seen in some areas while in others there is a relative lack of a capillary bed. Organised secretions occlude

bronchiolar lumina and there is hyperplasia and squamous metaplasia of the bronchial epithelium. These latter features are probably associated with the positive pressures used in ventilation and are difficult to disentangle from those related to oxygen administration.

These abnormalities develop most readily in the most immature lungs, particularly in association with air leaks. Preventative measures include the use of adequate ventilation to reduce the ambient oxygen requirement, while avoiding high ventilatory pressures if possible. Avoidance of air leaks by appropriate ventilation including patient-triggered ventilation is equally important.

Retinopathy of Prematurity (ROP)
This condition, previously known as retrolental fibroplasia, was first recognised in 1940 in the U.S.A. It came to public notice in the 1940s and 1950s when its occurrence and the major consequence — blindness — reached almost epidemic proportions in surviving premature infants, particularly in the U.S.A. At that time the condition was thought to be caused purely by oxygen toxicity. Since the 1970s the frequency of the disease has increased again in the 'new' population of surviving premature babies, <28 weeks gestation or <1000g birth weight. It remains the commonest cause of blindness in the neonatal period, although it is now very unusual in infants >32 weeks gestation.

The disease is recognised in the perinatal period by indirect ophthalmoscopy and this is now performed on at risk babies in many Neonatal Units. Milder grades of severity are common, and 80-90% regress spontaneously. They are probably of little importance. Occasionally, however, they progress to severe disease (cicatrical ROP) leading eventually to distortion and detachment of the retina. Treatment by cryotherapy or laser therapy may arrest progressive disease.

The relationship with oxygen is probably a complex one. Retinal blood vessels grow out to the periphery during gestation but do not reach the temporal margin until after term. High levels of local tissue oxygenation cause spasm of these vessels and ischaemia of the retinal periphery. Subsequently, new, poorly organised blood vessels proliferate from remaining central vessels and attempt to revascularise the periphery. Bleeding and retinal detachment can follow, the time interval between initiation of disease and damage averaging 4-6 weeks.

Damaging effects of local oxygen in the pre-term infant are probably exaggerated because of the poor function of oxygen-generated free radical scavengers in this population. Thus the level of retinal PaO_2 causing damage may vary. It is widely recommended that PO_2 should be kept below 12kPa, as a practical measure.

Other factors than oxygen are associated with ROP possibly through direct effects on retinal vasculature; they include intraventricular haemorrhage, hypoxia, apnoeas, hypocapnia (producing intracerebral vasoconstriction) and the use of indomethacin. A variety of potential preventative agents, particularly vitamin E, have not currently been proved to be effective.

HYPO- AND HYPERCAPNIA

The normal PCO_2 in the neonate is 4.0-5.0 kPa. A low PCO_2 is uncommon in a spontaneously breathing baby. The commonest cause is overventilation secondary to metabolic acidosis. Over-ventilation can also occur in spontaneously breathing babies with cerebral irratibility due to birth trauma or birth asphyxia. An increased PCO_2 is usually due to hypoventilation, either primary or secondary to metabolic alkalosis.

ACIDOSIS AND ALKALOSIS

A normal pH in a healthy term baby is 7.30-7.40 in the first week of life (Table 9.2). Low pH is undesirable for a variety of reasons. In the pre-term baby acidosis may prolong patency of the ductus arteriosus, and may make the baby more susceptible to cerebral insults. Severe acidosis itself produces reduced peripheral perfusion and can prolong or produce pulmonary hypertension and right-to-left intracardiac shunting of blood.

As stated earlier, the commonest cause of acidosis is lactic acidosis as a consequence of poor perfusion. If hypovolaemia is thought to persist, the primary management of such a baby would be administration of colloid in adequate volumes (e.g., 15-20 mL/kg body weight).

The metabolic component of acid-base disturbances can be assessed from calculation of the bicarbonate and base excess (which may be negative i.e., a base deficit) in freely flowing blood. A commonly used formula to assess the amount of base required for correction is the following:

Base required = 0.3 x body weight (kg) x Base deficit (mmol)
= mmol bicarbonate required

Usually half this amount is given as diluted (4.2% maximum) sodium bicarbonate solution into a large vein.

Major changes in perfusion and cardiac output may follow such therapy, and therefore it should only be used in situations where the acidosis is severe and likely to persist without treatment, and should be given over at least one hour except in acute emergency.

FURTHER READING

Duc G, Sinclair JC. Oxygen administration. In:

Effective care of the newborn infant. Sinclair JC and Bracken MB. Oxford Publications, 1992: 178-199.

Koch G, Wendel H. Adjustment of arterial blood gases and acid base balance in the normal newborn infant during the first week of life. Biol Neonat 1968; **12**: 136-141.

Silverman WA. Retrolental Fibroplasia; A modern parable. Monographs in Neonatology 1980; Grune and Stratton, New York.

Walter JH. Metabolic acidosis in newborn infants. Arch Dis Child 1992; **67**:767-69.

Wigglesworth JS. Perinatal pathology: Major problems in pathology 1984; Vol 15: 192-194. WB Saunders Co., Philadelphia.

Chapter 10

Requirements for a Clinical Biochemistry Service for the Neonate

INTRODUCTION

Biochemical monitoring of babies in the hospital wards is usually restricted to plasma bilirubin measurement in jaundiced babies and occasionally an accurate blood sugar measurement to confirm the result of a screening test. Urine is often analysed for reducing substances in jaundiced babies as a crude screen for galactosaemia and this may be done at the bedside or in the laboratory.

Most District General Hospitals will have a Special Care Unit (see p 2) and the clinical biochemist will need to make provision for an appropriate service for investigation and monitoring of prolonged neonatal jaundice (see p 27), respiratory disorders, infection and care of the very low birthweight baby. If more specialist clinical care is provided, e.g., parenteral nutrition or neonatal surgery, then additional biochemical support will be required.

Neonatal Intensive Care Units are usually situated in major teaching or sub-regional centres as part of a specialist maternity/paediatric service. Babies in these units, by definition, will require more frequent and specialist clinical biochemistry support.

SPECIMEN NEEDS

BLOOD

The term neonate has a total blood volume of approximately 275mL, whereas in a premature infant weighing 1kg the blood volume is only 80mL. Due to the high haematocrit in the neonate, the plasma yield from a given blood volume in a neonate is lower (approx 30%) than that obtained in the older child or adult (Fig 10.1) and 10mL of blood, perhaps collected as several different specimens over a few days, is an appreciable percentage of the baby's total blood volume (Fig 10.2)

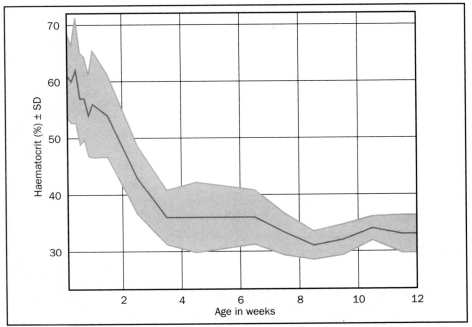

Fig 10.1   Haematocrit in the term neonate and young infant

The need for ultra-micro technology is therefore paramount and the necessity for repeat blood collections on the same baby should always be questioned, especially for the very low birth weight baby. Sufficient volumes of blood for most 'routine' tests can be collected by capillary puncture of the heel. It is usually possible to collect 600μL blood (i.e., two plastic tubes such as Sarstedt Microvette CB300 tubes) by this route, which should be sufficient for the most commonly requested analyses, e.g., bilirubin (total and conjugated), creatinine, sodium, potassium, albumin and calcium. Great care must be taken to choose a part of the heel which will produce minimum risk of damage to the bone and suitable lancets with short tips should be used (see Protocol A p 182). In the neonate, the vascular bed of the foot is located between 0.35 and 1.6mm from the surface. Complications of heel pricks include bleeding of the puncture site, infection of bone, cartilage or skin and generalised blood stream infection. Repeated punctures of the same site should be avoided.

After collection, blood should be suitably protected from light if bilirubin analysis is required. Blood gas analysis requires collection into capillary tubes and transport in iced water if analysis is not to be immediate.

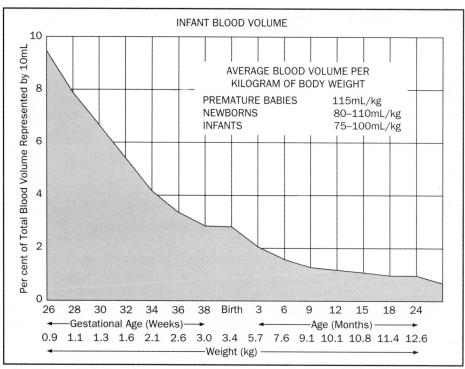

Fig 10.2   Relationship of a 10mL blood sample to total blood volume

Capillary puncture and subsequent blood collection is a skilled procedure to ensure a quality specimen and in particular to minimize haemolysis. It can be particularly difficult and labour intensive in a very small baby. A badly collected specimen which has been obtained by excessive squeezing and scraping of the tube across the skin is likely to be grossly haemolysed and be contaminated with tissue fluid and sweat. Results obtained from such specimens will therefore reflect release of electrolytes from red cells, especially potassium and magnesium; dilution with tissue fluid, e.g., a falsely low albumin, sodium etc., and contamination from sweat, e.g., falsely high ammonia and certain amino acids. Even without obvious visible haemolysis, potassium concentration in capillary plasma may be artefactually raised and on average is 1.0-1.5mmol/L higher than in arterial blood, although wider discrepancies can occur. The limitations of capillary blood should not be underestimated and, when possible, venous blood should be collected by the medical staff. However, capillary specimen collection

Table 10.1 Clinical biochemistry analyses usually available on blood obtained by capillary puncture

• Alanine transaminase	• Gamma-glutamyl transpeptidase
• Albumin	• Glucose
• Alkaline Phosphatase	• Hydrogen ion (pH)
• Aspartate transaminase	• Osmolality
• Bicarbonate	• Phosphate
• Bilirubin	• Potassium
• Calcium	• Sodium
• Chloride	• Total protein
• Creatinine	• Urea

is best performed by trained laboratory-based personnel. This arrangement has the advantage of having a semi-permanent and skilled team available who become experts and appreciate the difficulties of capillary puncture in the neonate. Any tendency by laboratory personnel for 'insufficient blood' to roll off the tongue is minimized by the appreciation of the blood collection procedure and the knowledge that it is probably themselves or a close colleague who have to go back to repeat the procedure.

When collecting small volumes of blood via an arterial line, particular care should be taken to aspirate and discard any infusion fluid in the line and then flush the line with sufficient blood volume; erroneous results can occur because of a dilution with the infusion solution.

DRIED BLOOD SPOTS
Some tests (neonatal screening, see p 85) can be performed on fluid eluted from discs punched out from dried blood spots, each usually containing about 5-10µL whole blood. Careful collection is required to avoid contamination from sweat and to ensure that each circle is appropriately filled. Both inadequate and 'over-filled' blood spots can lead to erroneous results.

URINE
The best way of collecting urine from a neonate is to use the 'cotton wool ball' technique with a plastic glove. Three or four clean cotton wool balls are placed in a thin plastic disposable glove. The neck of the glove is folded over several times

and strategically placed around the genitalia so that the urine passes into the glove and soaks the cotton wool. If necessary the top of the glove can be secured gently using thin plastic tape (e.g., Dermiclear or Transpore). When wet, urine can be readily aspirated from the cotton wool using a plastic 5mL syringe and transferred into a clean plastic universal bottle. Up to 20 mL urine, depending on the number of cotton wool balls used, can be collected in this way. Alternatively a plastic urine bag can be secured on the baby but this has the disadvantage that the baby's skin may become sore from the adhesive and is not suitable if repeated urine specimens are required.

The newborn baby passes less than 100mL urine per day (Table 10.2) and hence small losses from a timed collection are significant.

Table 10.2 Daily excretion of urine

Age	Volume (mL/day)
Full term newborn, 1–2 days	15–60
2 months	250–450
6–8 months	400–500
1–2 years	500–600
2–4 years	600–750
5–7 years	650–1000
8–15 years	700–1500
Adult	1000–1600

SWEAT

Testing for cystic fibrosis by measurement of sweat sodium and chloride (see p88) should be deferred until the baby is at least four weeks of age if possible. This usually enables sufficient sweat to be collected whereas testing earlier may only result in the test having to be repeated because inadequate sweat was obtained. If earlier testing is particularly important, because of maternal anxiety or because a decision to perform invasive investigations rests on the result, then the test can be performed. Reliable results may be obtained provided there is sufficient weight of sweat and an adequate sweat rate.

FAECES

Faeces may be required, e.g., for detection of reducing sugars, occult blood, or examination for excess fat. The small quantities required can usually be obtained by scraping from the nappy

TEST AVAILABILITY / WORKLOAD SIZE

With a few exceptions the most commonly requested clinical biochemical tests for the Neonatal Unit are the same as those in use for paediatric and adult clinical biochemistry. If neonatal tests are being performed within a laboratory providing a large number of analyses for adult patients, special arrangements may need to be made to provide appropriate sample processing, methods and turnaround time for the neonatal patients.

On site or nearby biochemical services will predominantly involve micromethod analyses of sodium, potassium, blood gases, glucose, creatinine, calcium and bilirubin in blood with rapid turnaround on a 24 hour/day, 7 day/week basis. Frequent requests for albumin, liver enzymes, direct (conjugated) bilirubin and alkaline phosphatase, as well as urinary electrolytes, will be generated by all but the smallest units. The workload generated by Birmingham Maternity Neonatal Unit is shown in Table 10.3. The sick neonate is often in a very labile condition and can deteriorate extremely rapidly and therefore the facility to provide a rapid turnaround time for selected tests is essential.

Those tests for which an emergency service may be required are listed in Table 10.4 together with a specification of turnaround time required. A rapid system for result transmission to both Special Care and Intensive Care Units is essential. Where workload is large this could take the form of a direct computer link from the laboratory to a VDU located in the Unit.

OUT OF HOURS SERVICE

Methods used out of hours should not give different results to those used during the day. This is particularly important when 'following' plasma bilirubin and/or sodium. Some 'electrolyte' analysers using ion specific electrodes may give significantly different results to others and there are notorious differences in accuracy between some bilirubin methods.

The out of hours workload for clinical biochemistry from a major neonatal teaching unit will be in the region of 1000 requests per annum with the most frequent request being plasma bilirubin and the majority of work requested before midnight. This assumes that 'cotside' acid base analysis is available and undertaken by the junior medical staff.

Table 10.3 Annual clinical biochemistry workload at Birmingham Maternity Hospital (1991-1992)

General Wards (5000 deliveries/year)

Total requests	4491
Total tests	8323

Neonatal Unit (6 intensive care cots: 500 admissions/year)

Total requests	7356	(includes 793
Total tests	37127	requests out of hours)

Individual Tests

Blood gases	9500
Bilirubin	8000
Sodium, potassium	5500
Creatinine	4500
Albumin	4500
Alk Phosphatase	1500
Glucose	800
AST	700
CSF biochemistry	100

NEAR-PATIENT TESTING

Glucose monitoring using BM-Stix is required on a regular basis. Low results (<2mmol/L) must be checked by a quantitative laboratory method. The greatest requirement for 'cotside' testing for the neonate is assessment of acid base status. Special Care Units can justify the provision of a dedicated acid base analyser and in some units, depending on size, availability of equipment for sodium, potassium and ionised or total calcium analyses may be appropriate.

The use of these instruments by medical and/or nursing staff *must* be under the control of the laboratory, and the same standards and guidelines as for all laboratory equipment based outside the laboratory should apply, such as those cited in the Joint Working Group on Quality Assurance Guidelines. It is particularly important to provide laboratory support for equipment maintenance and troubleshooting, and adequate backup in the event of instrument failure.

Table 10.4 Specification for turnaround times for 'Routine' and Urgent services

Analysis	'Routine' Service	Urgent
Blood gases :— For intensive care	Stat	
For other purposes	10–20 minutes	
Bilirubin	1–2 hours	<1 hour
Sodium, potassium	1–2 hours	30 minutes
Calcium	1–2 hours	30 minutes
Creatinine, urea	4 hours	<1 hour
Glucose	1–2 hours	<1 hour
Alkaline phosphatase	2–3 x weekly	Seldom required
Liver enzymes (e.g. Alanine amino transferase)	Same working day	Same working day
Phosphate	Same working day	Seldom required
Magnesium	4 hours	<1 hour if required
Ammonia	Analysed immediately	–
Lactate	5 working days	Same working day
Amino acids	5 working days	Same working day
Organic acids	5 working days	Same working day
17OH-Progesterone	1-2 working days	Same working day

There are a variety of bench-top bilirubinometers available; in the authors' experience these do not provide an accurate or precise measurement of plasma bilirubin and are not recommended for use for monitoring neonatal jaundice.

Hand-held meters for transcutaneous measurement of bilirubin are available. Such meters are neither accurate nor precise and are highly dependent on skin colour. They can however be used to monitor trends in bilirubin concentrations in an individual baby as an adjunct to plasma measurement. The development of biosensors has not reached a stage where they are available on a practical level for neonates/infants. *In vivo* monitoring of glucose, bilirubin and acid base status would be of potential advantage in certain situations.

METHODOLOGY

Numerous clinical biochemistry analysers are now available with sample requirements of 10μL or less for each test. The choice of instrument must include consideration of 'dead volume' requirement and facilities available to minimise specimen evaporation (e.g., 'capped' specimen tubes, refrigerated sample units).

Potential error due to evaporation is particularly important where very small volumes are used. A small specimen not protected can evaporate by 10% in one hour and by as much as 50% over four hours. Because capillary blood is used extensively and because many babies are jaundiced, methods which have no or minimal interference from haemoglobin and bilirubin are desirable and should influence choice of technology. Classic examples are the interference of haemoglobin in some bilirubin methods and the interference of bilirubin in some creatinine methods.

Additional problems relate to sensitivity of methodology required, e.g., the normal 'low' creatinine values during the neonatal period and early infancy.

Great care must be taken when a neonate moves from one hospital to another whether to check with the clinical biochemist, any apparent difference in the value of a particular analyte may be methodological or because of different reference ranges. The classic example is alkaline phosphatase. Laboratories should be actively encouraged to change from King-Armstrong and other 'old' methodologies to the internationally accepted Scandinavian method to avoid serious problems with interpretation.

BIOCHEMICAL CHANGES IN THE PERINATAL AND NEONATAL PERIODS

The birth process and adjustment of the newborn to independent life have a major effect on the production, metabolism and excretion of many metabolites, hormones and enzymes. Rapid growth and maturation, particularly of the liver and kidney, further modify these parameters over ensuing weeks.

Consequently, the reference ranges for biochemical analytes in neonates not only differ from those in infants and older children, but many of them change significantly during the first four weeks of life. Superimposed on this changing physiological background are differences related to solute intake, e.g., breast or bottle feeding, which make an additional contribution to reference range variability. It is particularly important to appreciate these changes when interpreting the results of biochemical tests in the neonate.

Available data on reference ranges are limited for ethical and logistical reasons; they often relate to cord blood or blood collected at around six days of age as part of the neonatal screening programme. Historical data are often invalidated because of changes in instrument technology / methodology. The reference data provided in the Appendix (p 192) are intended to be a guide and are nosubstitute for good data produced by the local laboratory. The following illustrate some of the major changes which affect reference ranges.

THE BIRTH PROCESS

The stress of the birth process provides the 'kick start' which the baby requires to begin the process of adaptation to survival outside the womb. This stress response brings about marked changes in hormone secretion and concentrations of TSH, thyroxine and cortisol are markedly increased in the first 24 hours of life. In response to these processes, the term baby is thereby able to mobilise fuel and regulate metabolism. In contrast, the pre-term or small for gestational age baby has a much poorer ability to regulate metabolic processes for energy production.

The physical process of birth causes release of enzymes from muscle. There is a rapid and marked rise in plasma creatine kinase activity immediately after birth, followed by a decline over the first week. Awareness of this phenomenon is important when investigating for Duchenne muscular dystrophy.

MATERNAL CONTRIBUTIONS

If the mother has any abnormal biochemical results at delivery e.g., azotaemia secondary to pregnancy-induced hypertension, elevated bilirubin due to pregnancy associated liver dysfunction, then the initial results on the baby will mimic the mother's.

Concentrations of hormones, metabolites and proteins which are maternal in origin fall sharply after birth. 17-hydroxyprogesterone and cortisol show a fall over the first 24- 48 hours following birth. Use of these parameters for diagnosis e.g., of congenital adrenal hyperplasia, is therefore difficult in the first few days of life. As the infant begins to increase its own synthesis of proteins, e.g., immunoglobulins, caeruloplasmin, the concentrations gradually increase over the ensuing weeks or months.

FEEDING REGIME

Plasma urea is higher in formula fed than breast fed infants and some amino acid concentrations differ dependent on whether the milk is predominantly a curd, or a curd and whey formula, reflecting the protein content of the regimen. Plasma and urinary osmolality vary according to the overall solute load.

Many of the reference values commonly used were derived when infant feeding regimes had higher protein contents than currently used and so may no longer be applicable.

MATURATION OF ORGAN FUNCTION

Changes in kidney function have a marked effect on reference ranges for plasma creatinine and therefore will be dependent on gestational age as well as actual age (see Ch 4). Renal tubular function matures over the first six months of age, so there are markedly different ranges for urinary amino acid and phosphate excretion during this period.

Some proteins (e.g., α-fetoprotein) and enzymes are specific to the fetus and are not produced by the baby. Deficiency of the fetal isoenzyme of cytochrome C oxidase may be responsible for a transient lactic acidosis in infancy. This phenomenon may account for other, as yet undocumented, transient 'abnormalities' which spontaneously resolve as the infant matures. Relative immaturity of liver enzyme systems will cause a different profile of metabolites at different ages. For example, the stressed premature baby will have increased concentrations of cortisol precursors, but not of cortisol, due to immaturity of the steroid synthesis pathway.

REFERENCE RANGES: A SUMMARY

The neonate has significantly different 'normal' ranges for many analytes (see Appendix p 192) compared with adults and even to infants/children. The clinical biochemist should play an active role in education to ensure that users of the service are fully aware of reference ranges for neonates *for those methods used in that particular hospital*. This will of necessity mean obtaining reference data from colleagues, to whom specimens are referred for the more specialist tests. This is an on-going activity as junior house staff come and go, and should be shared with the more senior clinical staff.

LIAISON WITH THE CLINICAL BIOCHEMISTRY LABORATORY

The clinician is more likely to receive a quality service if there is good and regular communication with the Clinical Biochemistry Department. The provision of a rapid and effective means of communication and designation of a particular contact person for the Neonatal Unit provides the best approach. The clinical biochemist should have regular contact, by way of contributing to ward rounds, case discussions and presentations, clinical audit, formulation of protocols for investigations and should be the link person between the clinical unit and the laboratory. In this way there can be a mutual understanding of clinical and laboratory problems which in the authors' experience leads to co-operation and encourages development of a service which benefits the clinician, the biochemist and, not least, the patient.

Investigation of patients for possible inherited metabolic disorders (see p 187) places particular demands on the laboratory and accurate and regular discussion is paramount. The clinical biochemist needs to be made aware of the urgency of the situation, to discuss and agree exactly what tests will be undertaken and when, to inform the clinician of when results are expected to be available, and to communicate these results. In a District General Hospital the biochemist may need to make arrangements to send plasma, urine and tissue specimens to a specialist laboratory for investigation. The biochemist is an important link between the DGH and specialist centre.

In return, the clinician must make the clinical biochemist aware of any new developments e.g., deterioration of the patient, development of new features which might change the priority for investigation, or suggest that different investigations are indicated. It is very demoralising for the clinical biochemist to have laboured for the majority of the day performing complex and demanding tests to discover, when telephoning results, that an alternative, non-metabolic diagnosis had been made earlier in the day.

Equally, the clinical biochemist must follow through his discussions with feedback to the doctor. If the test has 'gone wrong' and the result 'won't be available today after all', the doctor should be informed and not left hanging on waiting, only to discover on telephoning the laboratory at 6 pm that the biochemist has gone home.

IMMEDIATE NOTIFICATION OF RESULTS

There are certain abnormalities which, if not acted on rapidly, could lead to serious clinical sequelae including death. It is important to remember that an abnormal result may be due to procedural errors in sampling, such as blood being taken from the same limb as is receiving an i.v. infusion, or use of the wrong specimen tube, and thus the clinician needs to be informed as soon as possible.

On occasions, however, the abnormality will indicate an urgent clinical problem and laboratory personnel need to be aware of test values which must be immediately notified to the responsible clinician. Suggestions for such a list are in Table 10.5.

Table 10.5 Laboratory test values which must be immediately notified to the responsible clinician

Test	Plasma Value	Possible Symptoms / Complications
Sodium	<120mmol/L	Seizures
	>170mmol/L	Seizures, cerebral oedema
Potassium	>7.5mmol/L	ECG rhythm abnormalities, death
Phosphate	<0.3mmol/L	Myocardial dysfunction, respiratory failure, muscle weakness, seizures, death
Glucose	<1.7mmol/L	Seizures
Bilirubin	>400μmol/L	Kernicterus
Calcium	<1.5mmol/L	Seizures

COSTS

The reforms engendered by the UK Government White Paper "Working for Patients", have placed major demands on all parts of our Health Service to provide financial information. The cost of a laboratory request will include all components, from phlebotomy, where provided, to report generation. The various pre- and post-analytical components of the service i.e., advice on test selection, interpretation of results and advice on further investigation and management, all have to be costed as part of the clinical biochemistry service and will appear as part of the costs for the neonatology speciality. A study published at Birmingham Maternity Hospital has shown that clinical biochemistry accounts for approximately 7% of the total patient care costs, with an average cost per request of £5 (1989-1990 prices). Any proposals to drive laboratory costs down should take into account the special needs, both analytical and advisory, for neonatology and not compromise the quality of service to the patient or clinician. Equally important, as the NHS reforms progress, it will be important to audit the use of the clinical biochemistry service and to agree, if indicated, revised protocols for certain clinical situations.

FURTHER READING

Department of Health Circular HC (Hazard) (89) 31. Issued 17.10.89. Blood gas measurements: The need for reliability of results produced in extra-laboratory areas.

Druker RF, Williams DRR, Price WP. Quality assessment of blood glucose monitors in use outside the hospital laboratory. J Clin Path 1983; **36**: 948-953.

Marks V. Essential considerations in the provision of near patient testing facilities. Ann Clin Biochem 1988; **25**: 220-225.

Marks V. Near patient testing: Implications for laboratory-based professions. Med Lab Sci 1990; **47**: 326-329.

Newns B, Drummond MF, Durbin GM, Cully P. Costs and outcomes in a Regional Neonatal Intensive Care Unit. Arch Dis Child 1984; **59**:1064-1067.

Smith GC and Taylor CM. Recovery of protein from urine specimens collected in cottonwool. Arch Dis Child 1992; **67**: 1486-1487.

Welsh Scientific Advisory Committee. WSAC/D/1/84. The use of diagnostic equipment and procedures outside the diagnostic laboratory.

Chapter 11

Case Studies

CASE 1 — DYSMORPHIC FEATURES

The patient was a girl, the second child born to Asian parents who were first cousins. Although the baby was reported to be of normal size at 16 weeks gestation, serial ultrasound scans revealed her to be small, with a fall-off of head circumference at 26 weeks. At birth the child had Apgar scores of 6 and 7 at 1 and 5 minutes respectively and was noted to have a high forehead, with prominent anterior and third fontanelles, slightly rotated ears, a carp-shaped mouth and neck webbing. The child was very **hypotonic** with feeding difficulties and nystagmus. **Liver function was abnormal** with persistent jaundice (plasma bilirubin 92µmol/L at four weeks) and elevated aspartate aminotransferase (454 IU/L). The combination of dysmorphic features, liver dysfunction and hypotonia strongly suggested an inborn error of peroxisomal metabolism (see p 117).

Discussion

Zellweger's Syndrome was confirmed by demonstrating abnormal plasma concentrations of very long chain fatty acids, a deficiency of red cell membrane plasmalogens and low platelet dehydroxyacetone phosphate transferase activity. There is no treatment for this disorder and the child died at 75 days of age following an infection. Prenatal diagnosis is however available either by first trimester chorionic villus sampling at 8-11 weeks or by amniocentesis at 15-18 weeks.

Points to Note

- Some inborn errors of metabolism present with dysmorphic features in the neonatal period (see p 120) although more frequently chromosomal disorders, genetic syndromes or intrauterine trauma are the cause.

- The classical presentation of Zellweger's Syndrome is dysmorphic features, hypotonia and liver dysfunction. This may be the exception rather than the rule and in a neonate or infant with any two of these features a peroxisomal disorder should be considered.

CASE 2 — ACUTE LIVER FAILURE

A male Asian baby of consanguineous parents presented at three weeks of age with a heart murmur. He was admitted for 24h for cardiovascular investigation but no abnormalities were found. He was, however, noted to have a strange 'cabbage-like' smell and a urine sample was sent for amino acid investigations. The urine showed gross galactosuria (greater than 10g/100mL) and increased tyrosine and methionine. The child was reviewed one week later. He was well but in view of the urine results was admitted for further metabolic investigations. Galactose was again present in the urine and (because of the possibility of galactosaemia) the feeds were changed to the lactose-free formula, Wysoy. Other investigations at this time gave the following results:

Plasma alkaline phosphatase	2183 IU/L
Plasma alanine transaminase	50 IU/L
Plasma glucose	1.8 mmol/L
Plasma methionine	2463 µmol/L (normal up to approx 70)
Plasma tyrosine	1154 µmol/L (normal up to approx 100)
Prothrombin time	110s (12-14)
Partial thromboplastin time	75s (35-40)

Four days after admission he suddenly became very ill, acidotic, grey, pyrexial and had gross ascites with a very distended abdomen; plasma albumin concentration was 23g/L. He was commenced on treatment with intravenous dextrose, bicarbonate, antibiotics and fresh frozen plasma.

Possible metabolic causes for this type of acute liver disease presenting in the neonate or infant are:

- Classical galactosaemia
- Hereditary fructose intolerance (HFI)
- An organic acidaemia
- Tyrosinaemia type I

Classical galactosaemia was excluded by normal red blood cell galactose 1-phosphate uridyl transferase activity (noting that he had not received a blood transfusion which might have produced a false negative result). HFI is unlikely to present at this age because infant feeds do not usually contain fructose. Organic acid disorders were excluded by normal urinary organic acids. Succinyl acetone screen for tyrosinaemia type I was positive. The child was therefore treated with a special diet low in methionine, tyrosine and phenylalanine.

Discussion

Tyrosinaemia type I is an inborn error of metabolism inherited in an autosomal recessive manner. It is due to a deficiency of the enzyme fumarylacetoacetase which leads to the accumulation of succinyl acetone (see p 104).

Dietary treatment is based upon correcting the amino acid abnormalities in the blood in the hope that secondarily the toxic effects of succinyl acetone will decrease. Monitoring plasma amino acids, in particular tyrosine, methionine and phenylalanine is important.

Antenatal diagnosis is available by measuring the activity of fumarylacetoacetase in chorionic villus tissue or cultured amniotic fluid cells, and by measuring succinyl acetone in amniotic fluid supernatant.

A large proportion (in excess of 40%) of patients will develop hepatoma if they survive infancy. This risk is monitored by regular liver ultrasound, alphafetoprotein measurements and liver biopsy. Liver transplantation is now considered an appropriate treatment for this condition; it is clearly essential to provide good dietary and biochemical management for these patients until such time that transplantation is possible (see also NTBC treatment, p 105).

Points to Note

- Remember that an unusual smell is an indication for metabolic investigations.

- The presence of significant galactosuria is not always indicative of classical galactosaemia. The liver is the only organ in the body that is able to metabolise galactose, and therefore in the presence of significant liver disease, galactose is not cleared from the blood stream and appears in the urine.

- Hypoglycaemia is commonly found in patients with tyrosinaemia and occurs early on in the presentation, often before clinical evidence of liver disease.

CASE 3 — HYPERAMMONAEMIA

A baby girl was born at 38 weeks gestation after a normal delivery (Apgar 9 at both 1 and 5 minutes). She was small for gestation (<10th centile). Initially she fed well but at 32h was noted to be jittery and had developed expiratory grunting and tachypnoea (respiratory rate 52/min).

Feeds were stopped and she was transferred to the Neonatal Unit on 10% dextrose i.v. Preliminary laboratory investigations revealed no abnormalities, in particular acid base status was normal and there was no hypoglycaemia. Over the next 12h she developed convulsions, hypotonia and apnoea which required ventilation. She deteriorated rapidly and became entirely unreactive. At 48h the following metabolic investigations were performed:

Plasma ammonia	536µmol/L (normal <100µmol/L)
Urine amino acids	glutamine and alanine increased
Plasma amino acids	glutamine and alanine grossly increased
Urine organic acids	no abnormalities detected
CSF/plasma glycine ratio	normal

At 60h the baby became profoundly hypotensive and developed acute renal failure with acidosis and hypocalcaemia.

Quantitation of plasma amino acids, ammonia and urinary orotic acid were performed at six days of age when the baby was still not receiving any protein:

Plasma ammonia	183μmol/L		
Urine orotic acid	normal		**Normal**
		μmol/L	**range**
Plasma amino acids	glutamine	1915	(300-800)
	alanine	926	(150-400)
	arginine	5	(20-100)
	citrulline	not detected (20-60) (i.e., <5)	

no other amino acids were significantly abnormal, and in particular argininosuccinic acid was not detected.

Discussion

The initial hyperammonaemia, increased glutamine and alanine in plasma and urine and normal organic acids were strongly suggestive of a urea cycle defect (UCD). Citrullinaemia, argininosuccinic aciduria, argininaemia and ornithine carbamoyl transferase deficiency (see p 107) were excluded by the further investigations. The low plasma citrulline and normal orotic acid particularly suggested that this was likely to be carbamoyl phosphate synthetase (CPS) deficiency. At 14 days a liver biopsy was taken. Histology showed mild fatty change and **CPS activity was not detected,** thus confirming the diagnosis.

Points to Note

- Quantitation of plasma amino acids and urinary orotic acid are important tests in the differential diagnosis of urea cycle disorders. It is not possible to differentiate between a low and normal citrulline by qualitative assay.

- In urea cycle disorders, plasma ammonia, (183μmol/L on day 6 in this case) may not be grossly elevated if protein has been completely withdrawn. In this case the abnormal plasma amino acid concentrations (i.e., glutamine and alanine) were supporting findings.

CASE 4 — METABOLIC ACIDOSIS

A baby boy born after 38 weeks gestation by caesarian section, with an Apgar of 7 at 1 minute and 9 by 5 minutes, was transferred to the Neonatal Unit because there was concern about a possible narcotic effect of pethidine given just before delivery.

He made good progress until day 4 when he as noted to be tachypnoeic (respiratory rate 70/min). It was felt he probably had aspirated and he was thus commenced on antibiotics. Over the next 24h there was no improvement and laboratory investigations were undertaken as follows:

Arterial Blood

Hydrogen ion	42nmol/L	Std bicarb.	15mmol/L
Base excess	-14mmol/L	PCO_2	1.7kPa

Plasma

Calcium	1.57mmol/L	Sodium	145mmol/L
Magnesium	1.05mmol/L	Potassium	5.1mmol/L
Albumin	28g/L	Urea	9.6mmol/L
Glucose	2.8mmol/L		

On day 6 he developed jerking movements and apnoeic episodes and remained severely acidotic and hypocalcaemic despite attempts at correction. The most likely metabolic disorder in view of the acidosis was an organic acidaemia. A urea cycle defect however could not be excluded and blood and urine were taken for additional investigations with the following results:

Plasma ammonia	>400μmol/L
Plasma amino acids	lysine and tyrosine increased
Urine amino acids	no significant abnormalities
Urine orotic acid	normal
Urine organic acids (by GC/MS)	gross excess of methylmalonic acid

Other metabolites detected in excess:

lactate	2-hydroxybutyrate
acetoacetate	3-hydroxybutyrate
methylcitrate	4-hydroxyphenyl lactate

Discussion

The urine organic acid results were consistent with a diagnosis of methylmalonic acidaemia (MMA). The amino acid results were not specific. Increased plasma lysine has been reported in MMA and the increased tyrosine probably reflected some liver dysfunction. He was given a large dose of hydroxycobalamin i.m. but his condition worsened and he died on day 7. A skin biopsy was taken *post mortem* and investigations on the cultured fibroblasts confirmed that he had a deficiency of methylmalonyl CoA mutase which did not respond to vitamin B_{12} *in vitro*.

Points to Note

- Hyperammonaemia is a frequent finding in neonatal methylmalonic acidaemia. This illustrates the importance of investigating urine organic acids in a neonate with hyperammonaemia.

- Hypocalcaemia is a known complication of MMA. Other welldescribed features not identified in this case are hyperglycinaemia and glycinuria, hyperuricaemia and neutropenia.

- Skin biopsy taken *post mortem* is important for confirmation of the diagnosis. Characterisation of the deficit biochemically enables the option of prenatal diagnosis to be offered for future pregnancies.

CASE 5 — HYPOGLYCAEMIA

A full term male child, birth weight 3.62kg, was born to first cousin Asian parents. At 9½h of age the baby became hypoglycaemic (BM Stix <1mmol/L), hypothermic and refused feeds. He was transferred to the special care baby unit. At 17h he developed focal convulsions and was investigated as follows:

Arterial blood	hydrogen ion	52nmol/L
	PCO_2	3.3kPa
	Std bicarb.	14mmol/L
	base deficit	-12mmol/L

Plasma	bilirubin	<20µmol/L
	alanine aminotransferase	76IU/L
	creatinine	78µmol/L
	sodium	136mmol/L
	potassium	5mmol/L
	chloride	101mmol/L
	(anion gap)	26mmol/L
Urine	pH	5
	ketones	positive
	clinitest	positive
	clinistix	negative

Investigations for infection (chest X-ray, TORCH screen) were negative.

Discussion

The key biochemical findings were:

- hypoglycaemia

- metabolic acidosis (with acid urine)

- high anion gap

- ketonuria

- positive urinary reducing substances

Possible diagnoses based on these findings include (see protocol, p 188):

- Galactosaemia

- Tyrosinaemia type I

- Hereditary fructose intolerance

- Organic acid disorders

- Glycogen storage disorders

- Fat oxidation disorders

- Disorders of gluconeogenesis

- Hormone deficiency (adrenal insufficiency/hyperplasia)

Results of further investigations were as follows:

Galactose 1-phosphate
uridyltransferase screening test   normal

Blood	glucose	1.2mmol/L
	lactate	4.6mmol/L
	urate	431µmol/L
Plasma	amino acids	normal
Urine	amino acids	normal
	organic acids	increased lactate, 3-hydroxybutyrate and 2-oxoglutarate
	sugar chromatography	galactose detected

Insulin, cortisol and 17-hydroxyprogesterone were all normal.

A liver biopsy was performed which showed macrovesicular fatty change of hepatocytes with increased glycogen storage. Enzyme histochemistry showed positive staining for glucose 6-phosphatase and phosphorylase (i.e., activity detected). Hypoglycaemia, metabolic (lactic) acidosis, ketonuria and glycogen staining in the liver are strongly suggestive of a **glycogen storage disorder** (GSD), in particular type I presenting at this age.

Discussion

Patients with GSD type Ia have a deficiency of glucose 6-phosphatase demonstratable in fresh or frozen liver whereas type Ib show *normal activity in frozen liver*. The type Ib is due to a defect in the glucose 6-phosphate transport protein of the glucose 6 phosphatase system and can be demonstrated in *fresh liver*. A repeat biopsy with analysis on fresh tissue confirmed the diagnosis of type Ib glycogen storage disease.

Points to Note

- Hypoglycaemia with elevated blood lactate and ketonuria is strongly suggestive of glycogen storage disorders or defects of gluconeogenesis.

- Positive urinary reducing substances due to galactosuria can be positive in patients with liver dysfunction *not* due to galactosaemia.

- Glycogen storage type Ib tends to present as a severe form in the neonate. (Type 1 has been further subdivided and other subtypes may present in the neonate or infant).

- Definitive diagnosis requires enzyme assay on *fresh* liver biopsy.

CASE 6 — EXTREME PREMATURITY; DEHYDRATION

A 25 week gestation, 860g baby was delivered at a peripheral hospital. He was ventilated for hyaline membrane disease and given intratracheal exogenous surfactant treatment.

At 22 hours of age, despite 10% dextrose intravenously (60mL/kg/24h), he became hypoglycaemic. The infusion was changed to 15% dextrose. He was nursed under an overhead radiant heater. Fluid was increased to 90 mL/kg on day 2. On day 3 he was transferred to a specialized unit because of a persisting 100% oxygen requirement.

Table 11.1 Laboratory data for Case 6

	Day 1	Day 2	Day 3	Day 4	Day 5	Day 9	Day 12
Plasma							
Bilirubin/µmol/L		103	128	164	152	111	
Sodium mmol/L	147	154	162	153	145	128	134
Potassium mmol/L	4.8	3.5	5.9	5.6	3.7	4.0	3.9
Calcium mmol/L	1.47	1.91	2.05	2.18	2.40	2.27	2.27
Phosphate mmol/L		1.55					
Creatinine µmol/L	78	90	80	92	94	62	61
Glucose mmol/L	3.3	7.8		4.1			
Albumin g/L	26	24	31	31	25	31	28
Urine							
Sodium mmol/L			157	135	60	15	68
Potassium mmol/L			4.6	21	4	4	14
Creatinine mmol/L			.90	.74	.34	.33	.97

On transfer he weighed 735g (15% weight loss) and appeared very dry, with poor peripheral circulation. His biochemical results were as shown in Table 11.1. He had 2% glycosuria. Bacteraemia was diagnosed and treated with i.v. antibiotics.

He was given 15mL 4.5% albumin over two hours then maintenance intravenous fluid comprising 4% dextrose, 0.18% saline with added calcium gluconate at a rate equivalent to 150 mL/kg/day. Four hourly blood gas analysis was performed and ventilation adjusted accordingly. His weight was 770g on day 4.

Nutrition was supplemented with parenteral feeding through a percutaneously inserted silastic intravenous catheter from day 4, while enteral feeding with expressed breast milk containing added sodium chloride was introduced.

Points to Note

- Water loss through skin can be relatively huge in the very immature baby in the first 48 hours. Osmotic diuresis due to the excessive glucose administration exaggerated the situation in this case.

- Renal tubular immaturity produces obligate sodium losses even in the presence of hyponatraemia and whole body sodium depletion.

- Top up blood transfusion is frequently necessary in the small ill baby to replace blood losses resulting from the need to perform laboratory analyses. This baby's total blood volume was approximately 60mL.

CASE 7 — HYPOCALCAEMIA; HYDROPS FETALIS

A 29 year old mother had known anti-Kell antibodies. Ultrasound at 30 weeks' gestation demonstrated polyhydramnios with fetal hydrops i.e., ascites, pericardial effusion, cardiomegaly and subcutaneous oedema. After urgent crossmatch of compatible plasma-reduced blood an emergency caesarean section was performed. A 1.7 kg hydropic baby boy was delivered in poor condition (Apgar score 1 at 1 min), immediately intubated and ventilated and transferred to the Neonatal Unit. Cord blood haemoglobin concentration was 5.2 g/dL, direct Coombs' test was strongly positive.

An umbilical arterial catheter was inserted and immediate exchange transfusion of 80 mL/kg performed. After this, haemoglobin concentration was 11.7 g/dL.

Plasma bilirubin concentration was 70 μmol/L on cord blood, and 120 μmol/L post exchange. Double phototherapy treatment was commenced. By 16 hours of age, plasma bilirubin was 300 μmol/L and a second exchange transfusion was performed, using 160 mL/kg whole blood. Immediately post exchange plasma bilirubin concentration was 146 μmol/L, plasma sodium 144 mmol/L, potassium 4.7 mmol/L, calcium 1.75 mmol/L and albumin 26 g/L. Over the next six hours the baby became jittery and irritable. Twelve hours post exchange he had two obvious fits and was given phenobarbitone. Cerebral ultrasound scan showed no abnormality. Repeat plasma calcium concentration was 1.23 mmol/L. A slow i.v. bolus of 1 mmol/kg calcium gluconate was given.

A third exchange transfusion for hyperbilirubinanaemia was performed the next day. Calcium gluconate 1 mmol/kg was given post exchange. After calcium had been given, the plasma was 1.9 mmol/kg. Subsequent calcium and phosphate measurements were normal. There were no further seizures. The baby later required a fourth exchange transfusion, was extubated after four days, discharged home after seven weeks and has been physically and developmentally normal on follow up.

Points to Note

- Although rhesus incompatibility is the commonest haemolytic cause of hydrops in the UK, other blood group incompatibilities can occasionally be equally severe.

- Calcium supplementation should always follow exchange transfusion as the effects of anticoagulants in the transfused blood lead to hypocalcaemia.

- Seizures due to hypocalcaemia have a very good prognosis, in contrast to those associated with hypoglycaemia.

- Hypoproteinaemia makes analysis of total plasma calcium difficult to interpret.

CASE 8 — NEONATAL JAUNDICE, METABOLIC ACIDOSIS AND ANAEMIA

A baby girl was born after 42 weeks gestation to first cousin Asian parents. The couple had two other children, a six year old girl and a two year old boy, both of whom were well. The pregnancy was generally uneventful with delivery of a normal girl birth weight 3.76 kg with Agpar scores of 2 and 9.

There was meconium stained liquor during labour and the baby was intubated; spontaneous respiration was established by 5 minutes. B.M. stix was checked at 30 minutes (2mmol/L) and the baby transferred to the ward and started on milk feeds.

During the first 24 hours the baby was noted to be snuffly and had bouts of tachypnoea with a respiratory rate of 95/min. The baby was jaundiced, with a total bilirubin of 204 µmol/L. The B.M. stix results were low (1-2 mmol/L) despite 3 hourly feeds. The baby was assumed to have pneumonia; antibiotics were prescribed and feeds were stopped. She was placed on an i.v. dextrose drip.

At 35 hours she was still tachypnoeic and jaundiced, and a soft systolic murmur was noted. Arterial blood gases unexpectedly showed a partially compensated metabolic acidosis:

Arterial blood   hydrogen ion 66nmol/L   pH 7.18
PCO_2 2.6kPa
Base deficit -19mmol/L

The baby continued to be on no protein, with intravenous infusion of dextrose and bicarbonate.

There was no explanation for the metabolic acidosis and in particular no evidence of cardiac dysfunction or poor perfusion. In view of the possibility of a metabolic disorder as the cause, urine organic acids were investigated.

The baby continued on dextrose and bicarbonate, and the acidosis gradually normalised. The jaundice persisted and the baby became anaemic:

Day	Total bilirubin (μmol/L)	Haemoglobin (g/dL)
1	204	13.5
2	192	14.1
3	188	—
4	190	13.6
5	149	—
6	—	11.1

On day 7, urinary organic acids showed an abnormal peak of pyroglutamic acid and a diagnosis of **pyroglutamicaciduria** was made.

Feeds were cautiously re-commenced with supplementary bicarbonate and by day 9 the baby was generally much improved and on full feeds. On day 11 the baby became less well and on day 12 became pyrexial and had a fit. Analysis of cerebrospinal fluid revealed a high protein and low glucose concentration; *E.coli* was subsequently grown. Treatment with antibiotics was started.

The haemoglobin continued to fall, to 9.5 g/dL and 8.4 g/dL by days 12 and 13 respectively, despite a top up transfusion. The baby continued to be reasonably well, although tachypnoeic, on oral feeds with bicarbonate. However, on day 15 she became less well, not tolerating feeds, and had poor respiratory effort. She became unconscious, floppy and died that day. Her pH had fallen to 7.03 ($[H^+]$93mmol/L) with a base deficit of -15 mmol/L. A skin biopsy was taken for confirmatory tests. The diagnosis was confirmed *post mortem* by the finding of deficient glutathione synthetase in cultured fibroblasts.

Discussion

Pyroglutamic acid (5-oxo-proline) is an intermediate in the gamma-glutamyl cycle. This cycle leads to the synthesis of glutathione and a defect in the pathway, the most common being glutathione synthetase deficiency, leads to the accumulation of pyroglutamic acid.

Presenting features are haemolysis, leading to jaundice and anaemia, due to reduced red cell glutathione levels and metabolic acidosis caused by uncontrolled synthesis and consequent accumulation of pyroglutamic acid.

Pyroglutamic aciduria is a rare disorder, with less than 20 cases described in the literature. The cases described are heterogeneous although most cases have presented as an overwhelming neurololgical illness with fatal outcome. There is no proven treatment. It is possible that cases have been missed due to attributing death to overwhelming sepsis.

Points to Note

- Jaundice, haemolytic anaemia and metabolic acidosis in a neonate are characteristic of this disorder.

- Increased urinary pyroglutamic acid, although characteristic of this disorder, is not diagnostic of glutatione synthetase (GS) deficiency. There are several other causes of increased levels and enzyme analysis is required for confirmation of GS deficiency.

- Prenatal diagnosis is possible provided that the enzyme deficiency has been demonstrated in the index case (hence the importance of skin biopsy).

Protocol A

Capillary Blood Collection in the Neonate

GENERAL

Capillary blood collection from the neonate is not without risk and should therefore be minimised and planned in order to co-ordinate collection for both haematology and clinical chemistry. If specimens for both clinical chemistry and haematology are to be collected, then the blood for haematology collection must be collected *first*. (*Beware* possible contamination from potassium EDTA). This arrangement should minimise the extent to which the platelet count falls in shed blood after skin injury and provide results similar to those from a venous specimen.

Every attempt should be made to collect clinical chemistry specimens without haemolysis. This is possible even when great pressure is needed to obtain blood.

SELECTION AND PREPARATION OF SITE FOR SKIN PUNCTURE

Make sure that the baby is lying in a secure and comfortable position so that the heel is easily accesible. In children under one year of age the thumb and fingers should not be used for capillary blood collection. An area of heel, free from previous puncture sites, should be selected - see Fig.1. Check if the ankle has been used for venous access, as there is a danger of re-opening wounds. Punctures should not be performed on the posterior curvature of the heel where the bone is closest to the skin.

Before attempting any blood collection, the site should be warm and well perfused - this may be achieved by rubbing, immersion in warm (<40°C) water or wrapping in a warm nappy or towel (also <40°C). A dirty heel should be pre-washed with soapy water, rinsed and thoroughly dried.

The site must be cleaned with an antiseptic solution (isopropyl alcohol-"Sterets") and wiped completely dry with clean cotton wool to prevent haemolysis. Sterets can be used in an incubator; give a heel a quick wipe and then immediately remove the Steret from the incubator.

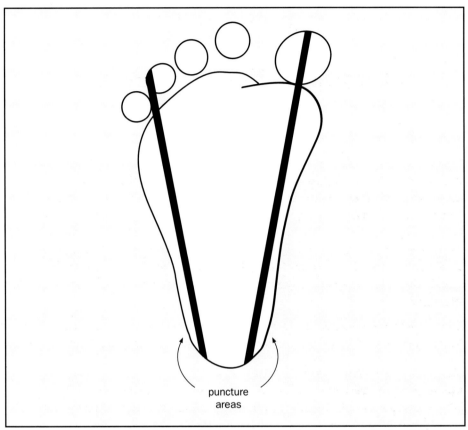

Fig 1   Diagram of foot to show recommended sites on the heel for capillary skin puncture

SKIN PUNCTURE

Before performing the puncture, check that all the necessary items are ready and in close proximity :

(i)   Steret

(ii)   lancet

(iii)   cotton wool

(iv)   specimen tube, e.g., Sarstedt Lithium heparin CB300

Check the name and registration number of the baby before starting the puncture.

Stand facing slightly away from the baby's head and hold the heel with the nearer hand. Grip the baby's heel firmly by holding around the ankle with the index and middle fingers so that the sole of the foot is against the palm of the hand and the heel exposed (see Fig.2). The thumb is placed around the heel and pressure in controlled with the thumb and index finger. Whilst maintaining tension on the heel make the puncture as one continuous deliberate motion in a direction slightly off perpendicular to the puncture site. Release pressure and wipe off the first drop of blood as it appears.

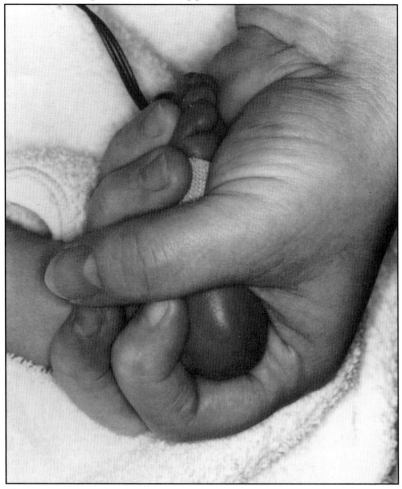

Fig 2   **Capillary skin puncture of the heel**

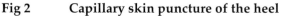

For a neonate the puncture depth *must not exceed* 2.4mm, and preferably be not greater then 1.6mm in the newborn, to avoid penetration of bone and hence the potential complication of osteomyelitis. Several devices are available (e.g., Safety Flow Lancet or Microlance, Becton Dickinson (UK) Ltd).

Hold the collection tube between thumb and forefinger. Obtain a hanging drop of blood and touch the side of this drop which faces away from the patient against the inside of the tube which is furthest from the patient. 'Pluck' off the drop of blood and knock it down to the bottom of the tube by giving the tube a sharp tap on a hard surface. Using a minimum of pressure, obtain further drops of blood and touch them against the same site inside the neck of the tube. They will follow the track of the initial drop. Pressure around the heel should be eased and then slowly and gently re-applied to allow more drops of blood to flow. Excessive 'milking' or 'massaging' is not recommended as this causes haemolysis. Should blood become smeared over the heel *during* the collection do not be tempted to scrape it off - wipe with clean dry cotton wool (*not* a Steret!) and start again.

Periodically flick the blood gently in the tube using the little or other free finger of the hand holding the tube. This is to ensure mixing of the blood with anticoagulant. Blood will flow more easily if the heel is held low.

The blood volume required is obviously dependent on which specific tests are required. This will vary for different laboratories dependent on the methods in use; it should be possible to obtain the most commonly requested tests (i.e., bilirubin (total and conjugated), sodium, potassium, creatinine, calcium and albumin) from a total blood volume of 500µL (see also Ch 10, p 153).

When the collection is finished, push the cap into the tube and invert gently several times to ensure mixing. Press a wad of dry and clean cotton wool firmly against the puncture site and hold the baby's heel above the body for a few minutes to stop the flow of blood. Plasters may be applied to the puncture site but are best avoided if possible; neonates have sensitive skin and a plaster which becomes detached is a potential for ingestion.

Make sure that the tube is labelled either with a felt-tipped pen or a narrow adhesive label as a 'flag' (i.e., wrap label around the tube close to the top so that a portion overhangs at the side).

1   If there are skin problems seek advice from a member of the medical team before going ahead.

2   Should a baby appear to be in a worrying condition before or during a blood collection, inform the doctor or nurse in charge who will advise whether to proceed. Similarly, if a baby's condition appears to have changed after the procedure inform the nurse or doctor in charge.

FURTHER READING

Blumenfeld TA, Turi GK, Blanc WA. Recommended site and depth of newborn heel skin punctures based on anatomical measurements and histopathology. Lancet 1979; I: 230-233.

Meites S, Levitt MJ, Blumenfeld TA, Hammond KB, Hicks JM, Hill GJ, Sherwin JE, Smith EK. Skin puncture and blood collecting techniques for infants. Clin Chem 1979; 25: 183-189.

Meites S. Skin puncture and blood collecting techniques for infants. . Update and problems. Clin Chem 1988; 34: 1890-1894.

Meites S, Hamlin CR, Hayes JR. A study of experimental lancets for blood collection to avoid bone infection of infants. Clin Chem 1992; 38: 908-910.

Slockbower JM, Jacoby H, Blumenfeld TA, Bruck E, Duffie ER, Mundschenk D. Approved standard procedures for the collection of diagnostic blood specimens by skin puncture. The National Committee for Clinical Laboratory Standards 1982; 2: 132-146.

Protocol B

Investigation of the Sick Neonate for Inherited Metabolic Disorders (IMD)

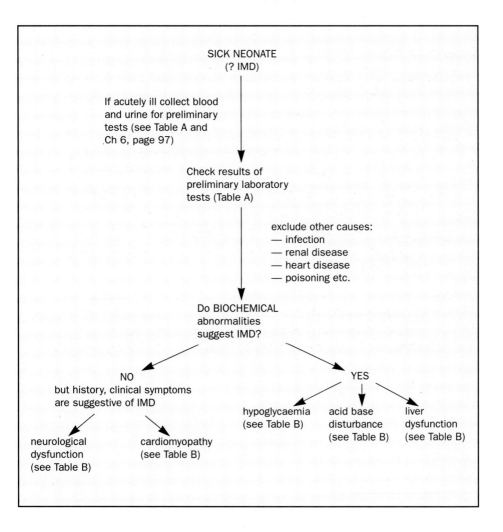

TABLE A. PRELIMINARY LABORATORY INVESTIGATIONS

Urine	smell
	reducing substances (Clinitest or Benedict's test)
	glucose (Clinistix or BM test strip)
	ketones (Acetest, Ketostix or Boehringer Mannheim test strip)
	pH (must be FRESH)
Blood	hydrogen ion, PCO_2, bicarbonate, base excess
	sodium, potassium, chloride
	calculated anion gap ([Na] + [K]) - ([HCO$_3$] + [Cl]) = (normally less than 20mmol/L)
	glucose (fasting, if hypoglycaemia not a presenting feature) — laboratory analysis, not BM stix
	calcium, magnesium
	bilirubin, alkaline phosphatase, alanine aminotransferase or aspartate aminotransferase
	creatinine (or urea)
	full blood count
	blood film

TABLE B. SPECIALIST INVESTIGATIONS FOR IMD IN THE SICK NEONATE

Presentation	Possible Metabolic Disorders	Suggested Investigations
Unexplained hypoglycaemia (see also pages 42 and 45)	Organic acid disorders Amino acid disorders Glycogen storage disorders (types I) Disorders of gluconeogenesis Congenital adrenal hyperplasia Congenital lactic acidosis Galactosaemia	Organic acids (U) Amino acids (U,P) 3-hydroxybutyrate (P) Free fatty acids (P) Lactate (P) Insulin (P) Cortisol (P) 17-hydroxyprogesterone (P) Galactose 1-phosphate uridyl transferase (B)
Acid base imbalance: – metabolic acidosis (exclude primary cardiac and respiratory disorders) – respiratory alkalosis	Organic acid disorders Congenital lactic acidosis Urea cycle disorders	Organic acids (U) Lactate (P) Amino acids (U,P) Ammonia (P) Orotic acid (U) Amino acids (U,P)
Liver dysfunction (often associated with hypoglycaemia and galactosuria)	Galactosaemia Fructose 1,6 diphosphatase deficiency Hereditary fructose intolerance Tyrosinaemia (type I) Glycogen storage disorders (type I) Disorders of Gluconeogenesis Alpha-1-antitrypsin deficiency	Galactose 1-phosphate-uridyl transferase (B) Sugars (U) Amino acids (U,P) Succinyl Acetone (U) Alpha-fetoprotein (P) Lactate (P) Oligosaccharides(U) Organic acids (U) Alpha-1-antitrypsin (P)
Neurological dysfunction: – seizures – depressed consciousness – hypotonia with Zellweger's syndrome Organic acid disorders	Non-ketotic hyperglycinaemia Urea cycle disorders Xanthine/sulphite oxidase deficiency Homocystinuria (remethylation defect) Congenital lactic acidosis	Amino acids (U,P,C,) Orotic acid (U) Ammonia (P) Urate (P,U) Sulphite (U) Lactate (P) Organic acids (U) Very long chain fatty acids (P)
Cardiomyopathy	Glycogen storage type II (Pompe's) Fatty acid oxidation disorders Tyrosinaemia (type I)	Lactate (P) 3-hydroxybutyrate (P) Free fatty acids (P) Oligosaccharides (U) Organic acids (U) Carnitine (P) Amino acids (U,P)

U = Urine   B = Whole Blood   P = Plasma   C = CSF

Protocol C

Emergency Specimen Collection for Suspected IMD

In life-threatening situations, where an inherited metabolic disorder is thought to be likely (either from family history, results of preliminary investigations or clinical presentation) the following specimens should be taken. At the earliest opportunity contact a specialist laboratory to discuss appropriate investigations. If possible, urine and blood specimens should be taken before death. Skin and tissue specimens are best taken as biopsy specimens when baby is still alive. If this is not possible, then they should be taken as soon as possible after death.

If any of the samples are taken after death it is extremely important to record accurately both the time of death and when the samples were taken. Appropriate storage as detailed below is **essential**.

URINE
Urine, *however little* is extremely useful. Ideally 5-10mL should be stored. Itshould be collected into a bottle with no preservative and stored deep frozen (-20°C or lower). If the sample is contaminated with blood, it should be centrifuged to remove cells before the supernatant is frozen.

BLOOD
5-10mL of blood should be collected in lithium heparin and 0.5mL in fluoride;the plasma should be separated as soon as possible and stored deep frozen (-20°C). Store the packed red cells at +4°C (do not freeze). If DNA analysis is likely to be required, a further 5-10mL whole blood (EDTA) in a plastic tube should be stored deep frozen (at least -20°C).

SKIN (FOR FIBROBLAST CULTURE)
Skin taken up to 24 hours after death is likely to be viable **provided it is not infected**. Take a skin sample and place it in suitable transport medium (obtainable from most virology or cytogenetics departments). In an emergency, sterile

isotonic saline can be used, **but agar should not be used**. The specimen should be stored at +4°C before despatch, and not frozen.

Sterility is of *paramount* importance when taking skin biopsy specimens, especially at necropsy.

IF INDICATED: TISSUE SAMPLES (LIVER, HEART MUSCLE, SKELETAL MUSCLE)

These should only be taken if there is a strong clinical suspicion of a primary defect in one of these tissues. **It is very important that blood and urine specimens are also taken and not just tissue specimens.** Necropsy tissue samples are usually only suitable for biochemical analysis if taken **within two hours of death**. Two or three needle biopsy specimens of tissue should be taken, placed in a plastic tube and snap frozen in liquid nitrogen (or solid carbon dioxide). The specimens should be stored deep frozen, as cold as possible.

Note that these samples are required for biochemical analyses only. Appropriate fixed samples may also be required for histological investigation.

CEREBROSPINAL FLUID

Sometimes a cerebrospinal fluid sample may be useful. If the specimen is cloudy or blood stained, it should be centrifuged and the clear supernatant stored deep frozen.

Appendix

Biochemical Reference Ranges

The values quoted below are a guide to interpreting data for term neonates, from birth to the age of four weeks, and apply to laboratory methods currently in use at Birmingham Children's and Birmingham Maternity Hospitals; they will not necessarily apply to methods in use at other Hospitals. Ranges will differ significantly for some analytes for different methods — consult your local laboratory.

Note: For information on reference ranges in infants and older children please refer to Insley (1990).

Acknowledgements
We are grateful to many colleagues who have contributed to the production of this Appendix, in particular to Neil Anderson at Birmingham Maternity Hospital, Julia Forsyth and Sue Williams at Birmingham Children's Hospital and to Brian Rudd, Geoffrey Holder and Angela O'Toole from The Women's Hospital, Birmingham for endocrinology data.

BLOOD/PLASMA	Unit	Reference Range	Comments
Acid base status:			
Hydrogen ion (pH)	nmol/L	40-45 (7.35-7.40)	Arterial
PCO_2	kPa	4.0-6.0	Arterial
Bicarbonate	mmol/L	18-25	
Base excess	mmol/L	-4 - +4	
PO_2	kPa	8.0-11.0	Arterial
Alanine aminotransferase			
(ALT)	IU/L	up to 40	Range will vary with method
Albumin	g/L	25-45	Depends on gestational age, levels increase over first three weeks.

BLOOD/PLASMA	Unit	Reference Range	Comments
Alkaline phosphatase (ALP)	IU/L	150-600	Higher levels first week due to placental ALP. Range can vary widely with method. Preterm levels higher (see p 73).
17α-Hydroxyprogesterone (17-OHP)	nmol/L	0.7-12.4	Note: There is a rapid fall from the very high concentrations of 17-OHP (maternally derived) in the first 24-48h of life. This is therefore an inappropriate time to measure 17-OHP for diagnostic purposes. Premature infants also have 2-3 fold higher levels of 17-OHP compared with values for full term infants.
α₁-Antitrypsin	g/L	0.9-2.2	'Adult' levels at birth, with fall after two weeks. Gradual rise to adult level by one year. Genotype should be assessed if <1.6g/L in infants with prolonged jaundice.
Alpha-fetoprotein	μg/L	50,000 - 150,000 100 - 10,000	Neonate one month (plasma half life 3.5 days)
Ammonia	μmol/L	up to 100	Preterm and/or sick babies may have concentration up to 200μmol/L. Lower level after one month.
Amylase	IU/L (Phadebas)	up to 50	Reference range for children reached after one year.
Anion gap i.e., ([Na⁺] + [K⁺]) - ([Cl⁻]+[HCO₃⁻])	mmol/L	less than 20	
Aspartate aminotransferase (AST)	IU/L	up to 100	Capillary blood. Range will vary with method.

BLOOD/PLASMA	Unit	Reference Range	Comments
Bilirubin (total)	μmol/L	up to 200	<10 days of age
(direct reacting)	μmol/L	less than 40	>10 days of age Jaundice (total bilirubin >50) after 14 days is abnormal.
Caeruloplasmin	g/L	0.08-0.23	0-4 months Increases from birth throughout the first year.
Calcium	mmol/L	2.15-2.75	After one week. There is often a marked fall after birth with lowest level (1.8) at around 24-48h of age.
Chloride	mmol/L	92-110	
Cholesterol (total)	mmol/L	1.5-4.0	Gradual increase from birth.
Copper	μmol/L	3-11	Rapid increase during first week.
Cortisol	nmol/L	<700	After 24h. Levels are high at birth. There is a marked fall within 24h following delivery — partly due to a fall in maternally derived contribution.
Creatine kinase	IU/L	High levels up to 10 × those in infancy/childhood.	Range dependent on methodology. Marked fall during first week of life, following peak at 24-48h.
Creatinine	μmol/L		Method dependent. Sharp decline in concentration over first month.

Postnatal age	Gestational age (weeks)			
	28	32	36	40
2 days	40-220	27-175	23-143	18-118
7 days	23-145	19-119	16-98	13-81
14 days	18-118	15-97	12-80	10-66
21 days	16-104	14-86	11-71	9-57
28 days	15-95	12-78	10-64	9-53

BLOOD/PLASMA	Unit	Reference Range	Comments
C-Reactive protein (CRP)	mg/L	up to 10	Plasma half-life 5-7h
Ferritin	µg/L	90-640	From two weeks (lower at birth). Falls to lower level by six months (upper limit 150).
Glucose (fasting)	mmol/L	2.0-5.5	For more detailed discussion of hypoglycaemia see p 40.
γ-Glutamyl transpeptidase (Gamma GT)	IU/L	up to 250 up to 150	During first two weeks. By one month; gradual decline over six months.
Immunoglobulins			
IgG	g/L	5.0-17.0	
IgA	g/L	up to 0.08	
IgM	g/L	up to 0.2	
IgE	U/mL	up to 5	
Iron	µmol/L	10-30	May be much higher at birth (up to 60)
Lactate (fasting)	mmol/L	0.5-2.0	
Magnesium	mmol/L	0.6-1.0	
Osmolality	mmol/kg	275-295	
Phosphate	mmol/L	1.3-3.0	Affected by type of milk feed
Potassium	mmol/L	3.5-6.5 3.5-5.5	Capillary blood Venous or arterial blood and not haemolysed
Protein (total)	g/L	54-70	Term baby. Gradual increase from birth. Pre-term babies have lower values.
Sodium	mmol/L	130-145	
Thyroid stimulating hormone (TSH)	mU/L	<10 (whole blood) <5 (plasma)	At 6 -14 days; pre & full term infants show a rapid increase in TSH during the first 24h
Thyroxine (total, tT4)	nmol/L	142-296 (1-3 days) 116-203 (1-4 weeks)	Higher levels occur in first week of life

BLOOD/PLASMA	Unit	Reference Range	Comments
Thyroxine (free, fT4)	pmol/L	14-28	Higher at 1-3 days
Transferrin	g/L	1.05-2.65	
Triglycerides (fasting)	mmol/L	0.3-2.0	
Triiodothyronine (fT3)	pmol/L	3-9	
Immunoreactive trypsin (IRT)	ng/mL	upper limit 70 (dried blood spot) upper limit 130 (plasma) 0-2 weeks	
Urea	mmol/L	1.0-5.0	Infants fed on cows milk formula may have higher levels
Urate	μmol/L	120-340	Values are higher at birth
Zinc	μmol/L	9-22	0-5 days Pre-term infants have higher values.

URINE	Unit	Reference Range	Comments
Calcium	mmol/kg/24h	less than 0.4	
Calcium:creatinine ratio	mmol/mmol	up to 1.2	Term baby; first two weeks
Copper	μmol/24h	up to 1.0	
Phosphate	mmol/1.73m²/24h	up to 2.0	Term baby; first two weeks Higher in pre-term babies
Fractional phosphate excretion	%	1-6%	Term baby; first two weeks Higher in pre-term babies
Potassium	mmol/kg/24h	up to 2	Depends on potassium intake and gestational age.
Sodium	mmol/kg/24h	up to 1 (full term) up to 3 (pre-term)	Depends on sodium intake and gestational age
Fractional sodium excretion	%	<0.3 term 2-5% preterm	During week 1

URINE	Unit	Reference Range	Comments
Urate:creatinine ratio	mmol/ mmol	up to 2.0	
CSF:			
Protein	g/L	0.4-1.2 0.2-0.8	Newborn Neonate
Glucose	mmol/L	2.5-4.5	Normally 75% of blood glucose

REFERENCES

1. Clayton BE, Jenkins P, Round JR. Paediatric Chemical Pathology : Clinical Tests and Reference Ranges. Blackwell Scientific Publications, Oxford, 1980.

2. Fleming PJ, Speidel BD, Dunn PM (Editors). A Neonatal Vade-Mecum. Lloyd-Luke, Sevenoaks, 1986.

3. Insley J. (Editor). Paediatric Vade Mecum. 12th Edition. Edward Arnold, London, 1990.

4. Lockitch JR, Halstead AC, Alberstein S, MacCallum C, Quigley A. Age and Sex Specific Paediatric Reference Intervals for Biochemistry Analytes as measured with the Ektachem-700 Analyzer. Clin Chem 1980; **34**: 1622-1625.

5. Meites S. (Editor). Paediatric Clinical Chemistry Reference (Normal) Values. 3rd edition. American Association for Clinical Chemistry, 1989.

6. Scott PH, Wharton BA. in: Textbook of Neonatology, 2nd edition, Biochemical Values in the Newborn, pp 1213-1229. Edited by N. Roberton. Churchill Livingstone, 1992.

Glossary

Adenoma	—	Benign tumour of epithelial origin, derived from glandular tissue or displaying glandular structures.
Agenesis	—	Failure of development (of an organ or body part).
Amniocentesis	—	Removal of specimen of amniotic fluid for analysis. Performed usually at 16-20 weeks gestation.
Anabolism	—	Build up of body tissues.
Apgar score	—	Widely used rapid assessment system of baby's condition after birth, usually at 1 and 5 minutes. The maximum score is 10.
Apnoea	—	Cessation of respiratory effort for a period longer than (usually) 20 seconds.
Ascites	—	Fluid in the peritoneal cavity.
Asphyxia	—	Failure of oxygenation and circulation.
Autonomic	—	Pertaining to the sympathetic or parasympathetic nervous systems.
Biliary atresia	—	Rare condition in which bile ducts disappear and there is progressive obstructive jaundice and liver disease.
Bradycardia	—	Drop in heart rate to below the normal range for age.
Catabolism	—	Breakdown of body tissues.
Centile chart	—	Chart derived from measurements (e.g., of weight) on large numbers of subjects. Lines on chart relate to centiles, i.e., number per hundred subjects whose measurement is above or below the line.

Cardiotocograph	—	Derived signal representing fetal heart rate.
Cephalhaematoma	—	Subperiosteal collection of blood over skull usually arising from trauma during delivery.
Choledochal cyst	—	Cystic malformation of major bile duct.
Cholestasis	—	Inadequate exretion of bile (e.g., due to obstruction, leading to its retention).
Chorionic villus	—	Area of fetal tissue in early pregnancy which will develop into part of placenta.
Colloid	—	Intravenous solution containing molecules between one and one hundred nanometres in diameter, e.g., albumin, dextrans.
Consanguinity	—	Degree to which a father and mother are also 'blood' relatives.
Coombs' Test	—	Red cells react with an anti-IgG reagent and clump together if they are coated with antibody (Coombs' positive).
Crystalloid	—	Intravenous solution which does not contain particles larger than one μm diameter.
Cyanosis	—	Blue discolouration of skin and mucus membranes due to an excess of deoxygenated haemoglobin in blood.
Cryotherapy	—	Treatment by freezing.
Dysmorphic	—	Unusual or pathological in shape.
Dysplasia	—	Abnormal development (of a tissue, organ or part of the body).
Encephalopathy	—	A condition affecting the functioning of the brain.
Endogenous	—	Arising from within the individual.
Enterocolitis	—	Inflammation of small and large intestine.
Epiphyses	—	Growing end points of bone.

Exogenous	—	Arising from outside the individual.
Exomphalos	—	Failure of return of intestinal contents to the abdominal cavity during early fetal life. There is no normal umbilical cord.
Fontanelle	—	The soft spots on top of a baby's skull wherethe bones do not meet. They become undetectable between 12-18 months.
Hepatomegaly	—	Liver enlargement. The liver is normally palpable just below the ribs in the newborn baby.
Hydrophobic	—	Water avoiding: molecules poorly soluble in water because of their hydrocarbon structure.
Hydrophilic	—	A substance with a strong attraction for water.
Hydrops fetalis	—	Description of a baby or fetus with effusions in several body cavities as well as under the skin. This can be caused by fetomaternal blood group incompatibility ('immune') or by a wide range of external or intrinsic problems ('non immune'). In the latter type, survival rates are poor.
Hyperoxaemia	—	PO_2 in blood which is above that thought optimal (8-12kPa).
Hypoplastic	—	Underdeveloped.
Iatrogenic	—	Caused by a medical agent or action.
Intrapartum	—	Occurring during labour or delivery.
Ischaemic	—	Receiving inadequate circulating blood.
Kell system	—	One of a number of blood group systems.
Kernicterus	—	Clinical condition associated with bilirubin toxicity to the brain. Cerebral nuclei are stained yellow.

Leucomalacia	—	Softness and white discolouration of an area of brain due to infarction and death of tissue.
Macroglossia	—	Large tongue.
Macrosomia	—	Large body, i.e., all organs are larger than usual.
Meconium ileus	—	Neonatal partial small intestinal obstruction due to abnormally sticky meconium. Usually caused by underlying cystic fibrosis.
Metaplasia	—	Change in cell type to one not typical of that part of the body.
Microcephaly	—	A small head.
Multipara	—	A women who has had previous pregnancies.
Natriuretic	—	Causing urinary excretion of sodium.
Necrotising enterocolitis	—	Inflammation of small or large intestine in neonate, sometimes leading to perforation or stricture.
Nephrocalcinosis	—	Calcification within the kidney.
Nephrogenesis	—	Production of nephrons (the units of renal function).
Neutropenic	—	Pathologically low number of neutrophils in blood.
Nullipara	—	A woman who has had no previous pregnancies.
Nystagmus	—	Abnormal repetitive eye movements.
Neuroglycopenia	—	Condition of neurological functional impairment due to insufficiency of glucose.
Oliguria	—	Rate of urine production below that expected (1-2mL/kg/hour in a neonate after the first week).

Opisthotonos	—	Posture where the neck and back are extended.
Oxytocin	—	Drug utilized in labour to promote contractions of the uterus.
Periventricular	—	Arising adjacent to the lateral ventricles inside the brain.
Pneumothorax	—	Leakage of air from the lung to the potential space between inner and outer pleura. The leaked air can then compress the adjacent lung and cause it to collapse.
Polycythaemia	—	Pathologically high haemoglobin concentration. Opposite of anaemia.
Polydipsia	—	Excessive water intake, usually due to thirst.
Pneumocytes	—	Specific differentiated cells lining the small airways and airsacs of the lung. Some produce surfactants.
Pyloric stenosis	—	Condition presenting at 2-3 weeks of age with recurrent milk vomiting due to progressive narrowing of stomach outlet. Treated by surgery.
Pyrexial	—	Feverish
Reye's Syndrome	—	A rare disorder of children, characterised by encephalitis and hepatic failure.
Rhesus incompatibility	—	Baby is affected when IgG antibodies cross the placenta from an immunized but unaffected rhesus negative mother. The antibodies destroy the baby's red blood cells if baby is rhesus positive.
Splenomegaly	—	Enlargement of spleen.
Surfactant	—	An agent reducing surface tension in the lung. A phospholipid with hydrophilic and hydrophobic poles forming a liquid surface lining to alveoli.

Systemic — Relating to the circulation through the body.

Tachycardia — Heart rate above normal (above 160 beats per minute in the neonate).

Tachypnoea — Respiratory rate greater than normal (40-60 breaths per minute in the neonate).

Torch screen — Antibody screen for congenital Toxoplasma, Rubella, Cytomegalovirus, and Herpes infection.

Vasodilatation — Opening up of blood vessels in an area of body in response to a stimulus.

Visceromegaly — Enlargement of the abdominal organs.

Index